D0998333

STURGEON

IS ALIVE AND WELL . . .

By the same author / A TOUCH OF STRANGE

MORE THAN HUMAN

THE SYNTHETIC MAN (*The Dreaming Jewels*)

WITHOUT SORCERY

E PLURIBUS UNICORN

A WAY HOME

STARSHINE

STURGEON

IS ALIVE AND WELL...

a collection of short stories by
THEODORE STURGEON

G. P. Putnam's Sons, New York

Copyright © 1971 by Theodore Sturgeon

Published by arrangement with the author

All rights reserved. This book, or parts thereof, must not be reproduced in any form without permission. Published simultaneously in Canada by Longmans Canada Limited, Toronto.

ACKNOWLEDGMENTS

"To Here and the Easel," copyright 1954 Ballantine Books, Inc.
"Slow Sculpture," copyright © 1970 Universal Publishing and Distributing Corp.
"It's You!" copyright © 1969 Knight Publishing Corp.
"Take Care of Joey," copyright © 1970 Sirkay Publishing Co.
"Crate," copyright © 1970 Sirkay Publishing Co.
"The Girl Who Knew What They Meant," copyright © 1970 Sirkay Publishing Co.
"Jorry's Gap," copyright © 1969 Knight Publishing Corp.
"It Was Nothing—Really!" copyright © 1969 Sirkay Publishing Co.
"Brownshoes," copyright © 1969 Knight Publishing Corp.
"Uncle Fremmis," copyright © 1970 Knight Publishing Corp.
"The Patterns of Dorne," copyright © 1970 Sirkay Publishing Co.
"Suicide," copyright © 1970 Knight Publishing Corp.

Library of Congress Catalog
Card Number: 70-136811

PRINTED IN THE UNITED STATES OF AMERICA

". . . Only the simplest go beyond
lucidities in season,
When hungry, eat, when tired, sleep,
and love for no reason."

To

JUDITH EISENSTEIN BAGAI
who keeps the faith

Contents

FOREWORD   9

TO HERE AND THE EASEL   13

SLOW SCULPTURE   72

IT'S YOU!   95

TAKE CARE OF JOEY   104

CRATE   115

THE GIRL WHO KNEW WHAT THEY MEANT   128

JORRY'S GAP   137

IT WAS NOTHING—REALLY!   149

BROWNSHOES   165

UNCLE FREMMIS   177

THE PATTERNS OF DORNE   195

SUICIDE   212

Foreword

Yes, I am alive and well.

Once to a perceptive friend I was bemoaning the fact that there was a gap in my bibliography from 1940 to 1946. (Actually some stories were published during that period, but only one had been written after 1940.) What wonders I might have produced had I not been clutched up, I wailed. And he said no, be of good cheer. He then turned on the whole body of my work a kind of searchlight I had not been able to use, and pointed out to me that the early stuff was all very well, but the stories were essentially entertainments; with few exceptions they lacked that Something to Say quality which marked the later output. In other words, the retreat, the period of silence, was in no way a cessation, a stopping. It was a silent working out of ideas, of conviction, of profound selection. The fact that the process went on unrecognized and beyond or beneath' my control is quite beside the point. The work never stopped.

I've held hard to that revelation in recent years, and no longer go into transports of anguish when the typewriter stops. I do other things instead, in absolute confidence that when that silent subterranean work is done, it will surface. When it does so, it does with blinding speed—a short story, sometimes, in two hours. But to say I wrote it in two hours is to overlook that complex, steady, silent processing and reprocessing that has been going on for months and often

9

years. Say then that I typed it in two hours. I do not know how long it took to write. I could only type it when it was finished.

I do not know if the package you hold in your hands will be regarded as remarkable in the bibliography. Biographically it represents a miracle, and engenders some tributes.

I was living at the bottom of a mountain in Neverneverland, far under a rock. Looking back on that time, I now know that I was unaware of just how far I had crawled and just how immobile my crouch. Suddenly one day there exploded a great mass of red hair attached to a laughing face with a beauty spot right in the center of her forehead and a totally electric personality. Her name was Wina and she was a journalist and a photographer and a dress designer and a dancer and she had traveled 6,500 miles with her cat (inside of whom she smuggled four kittens) to marry me. She crawled way in under that rock and hauled me out. We acquired a squirrel and some tropical fish and a baby (whose name is Andros Theodore, which means "Man is the gift of God," Lindsay Sturgeon) and set up housekeeping.

And suddenly I wrote. As I have said, I do not know how long it took me to write the stories, but I *typed* one a week for eleven consecutive weeks, and after a short hiatus, a twelfth—all while I was writing a novel. So the first tribute goes to Wina.

My next acknowledgment is to Tom Dardis, not simply for accepting the book for publication, but for agreeing to use this particular table of contents. For one thing I am delighted to have in one place exactly (with one exception) those "Wina" stories—but that's personal and sentimental. My most profound appreciation is extended to him for his willingness to include some of the stories which cannot be categorized "science fiction."

Science fiction is my best friend and my worst enemy. But for one or two notable examples, science fiction and science fiction writers are relegated to the back pages of the book review section, not to be taken seriously by serious critics. "I don't read science fiction," says Mr. J. Q. Public, with *On the Beach* and *Dr. Strangelove* and *Lord of the Flies* and *Messiah* and a half hundred others on the bookshelf behind him, and he marches out to see *2001*—all science fiction but never *called* science fiction and virtually never written by anyone who has ever appeared in *Analog* or *Galaxy* or *New Worlds* except, perhaps, in reprint, in some of the magazines which run reprints (and I'm glad they do). The predicament of the professional science fiction writer who takes himself and his work seriously could be called comic if it weren't for such unfunny things as hospital bills and the IRS, and why more of them aren't certifiably paranoid is a greater wonder than any of them have yet wrought. It seems a literal truth that to have acquired a reputation in science fiction is to be reflex- ively relegated to the twenty-fifth century with Flash Gordon and Buck Rogers, all wrapped up in a colored funny paper.

Yet the best writers in the field (as one of the cognoscenti once pointed out) write science FICTION, not SCIENCE fiction. Let me tell you something: you can not write good fiction about ideas. You can only write good fiction about people. Good science fiction writers are good fiction writers. When a blatant dabbler like Kingsley Amis gets three columns in *Time* magazine while nobody ever heard of a polished and thoughtful writer like Edgar Pangborn, it breaks my heart.

Very special thanks must go to two bright young editors, Merrill Miller and Jared Rutter, who bought most of the stories in this book. They asked me for stories. They didn't ask for science fiction or fantasy stories; they did not demand the currently obligatory skin scene—they just bought my stories as they arrived; and one can approach the typewriter with a wonderful sense of wingspread with a market like that.

Nothing will ever stop me from writing science fiction, but there sure is a plot afoot to keep me from writing anything else, and I won't have it. Perhaps now you can understand why I am so pleased with this collection.

My final tribute has to do with the one story in this book which is not the product of that astonishing summer. I wrote "To Here and the Easel" for a Ballantine book now long out of print. It was called *Star Short Novels*, and when Ballantine issued one of the three novels in a separate volume I knew it would not be reprinted, and asked and was graciously granted permission to use the story in another book. It was published in 1954 and has been seen nowhere else since.

T. S.

To Here And The Easel

Up here in the salt mine I've got a log jam to break.

And that about expresses the whole thing. I mix pigments like I mix metaphors; so why not? Who's a writer?

Trouble is, maybe I'm not a painter. I was a painter, I will be a painter, but I'm not a painter just now. "Jam every other day," as Alice was told in Wonderland, as through a glass darkly; "Jam yesterday and jam tomorrow, but never jam today." I know what I'll do, I'll paint for calendars; isn't this the '54 boom for the 44 bust? I'll skip the art and do handsprings eternal on the human breast.

So quickly: grab the brush, sling the oils; *en garde!* easel; you're nothing but a square white window to *me;* I'll throw a wad of paint through you so's we can all take a good long look inside. I'll start just *here* with the magenta, or maybe over *here,* and—

And nothing.

So down I go on the chair, I look at the canvas, it looks back at me, and we're right where we started. Didn't start.

Up here in the salt mine, as I began to say, I've got a log jam to break. The salt mine is my studio, studio being a name for a furnished room with a palette in it. The log jam is in my head. Why is it I can't work just because my brains are tied to a knot? "Giles," the maestro, the old horse's tail of a maestro

13

used to say to me, "Giles, don't paint with your brains. Paint with your glands," he used to say, "your blood. Sweat is a pigment. Dip your brush in—"

Shucks, Maestro! Get me a job in a sign shop. I'll sell everything else. Ad in the paper: for sale cheap, one set sable-tipped vesicles. One heart: ventricle, sinister; auricle, Delphic. Nine yards plumbing with hot and cold running commentaries, and a bucket of used carmine, suitable for a road-company Bizet-body.

Was a painter, will be a painter, ain't a painter. Make a song of that, Giles, and you can die crazy yelling it like Ravel chanting the Bolero, Ravel, unravel. Giles' last chants.

Ain't a painta, ain't a painta, ain't a painta *pow!* Ain't a painta, ain't a painta, ain't a painta *now!*

You better shut up, Giles, you're going to have another one of those dreams.

Well, I'll have it anyway, won't I? . . . the dreams, that's what's the matter with me. My glands I got, but my brains, they keep running off with me, glands and all. No not running off; more like a jail. I used to be a something, but I'm locked up in my own brains till I'm a nothing. All I have to do is figure a way out.

Or maybe somebody'll come and let me out. Boy, what I wouldn't do for somebody who'd come let me out. Anything. The way I see it, the other guy, the one in the dream, he's locked up too. I should figure a way out for him. So maybe he'll get on the ball and figure a way out for me. He was a knight in shining armor, he will be a knight in shining armor, but he ain't nothing but a nothing now. There shall be no knight. He got a prison turns night into eternal afternoon, with dancing girls yet.

I should get him out of a spot like that? What's the matter with a castle on a mountain with dancing girls?

On the other hand a knight who was a knight and who wants to be a knight is just a nothing, for all his dancing girls, if you lock him up in a magic castle on a magic mountain. I wonder if *his* brains are working str—

14

—aright because mine are sore churned. *Aiee!* and here the echoes roll about amongst the vaults and groinings of this enchanted place. No word have I, no shield, no horse, nor amulet. He has at least the things he daubs with, 'prisoned with him. And yet if he would paint, and cannot, is he not disarmed? Ay, ay . . . *aiee!* we twain are bound, and each of us enchanted; bound together, too, in some strange way, and bound nowhere. And whose the hardest lot? He has a brush; I have no sword, and so it seems his prisoning is less. Yet I may call my jailer by a name, and see a face, and know the hands which hold the iron key. But he, the 'prisoned painter, languishes inside himself, his scalp his fetters and his skull his cell. And who's to name his turnkey?

Mine I can name; he comes now, soft leather awhisper on marble, his very stride abhorrent magic, the pressures of the unalive against the never-living. Atlantes, hated Atlantes, of the soft eyes and stone mouth, Atlantes who, controlling me, would alter fate itself.

"Rogero, is all well with thee? Such a cry . . . like a great wind tearing the rocks." (His beard is full, he is too wise, he has no soul.)

"Ay, all is well!" I tell him scornfully. "Would I were such a wind, to tear and be torn on the rocks, and gladly, under the open sky; and never again to know a slow death of silks and sweets and boredom, the like of this . . . give me my sword."

"Ay, I will. And an enchanted shield to blind thine enemies, and a steed to master earth and air; this castle to shelter thee and all in it for thine own, and my powers for thy convenience—and all for a word."

Atlantes is tall; yet, rising, I may make him lift his beard to face me. Going to him, thunder-furious, I may come close, yet unlike other men he will not flinch. I may not strike him, nor anyone here nor any thing, so cautiously is he be-magicked. "For a word!" My voice stirs the hangings and sets the great stone halls athrum. "You call my faith a word, my fealty, my every drop of blood and all my days. I will never be your knight, Atlantes."

And of all things, I hate his smile. "Thee will, Rogero, unless thy choice is to languish here forever instead. My plans for thee are better ones than fate dictated," he says, and laughs at me. His voice booms inside my skull as my voice boomed a moment ago within the castle. "This is thy destiny, knight: that a maiden shall free thee, and that through her thou shalt embrace a new faith of sobriety and humility, and spend thy days accursed with earthbound slowness like a tortoise, dressed like a wren-hen; swordless and somber and chained."

I think about this, and look at the carvings, the silks, the aromatic mounds of fabulous fruits. At last, "Maiden?" I ask.

"Just the one for such adventures," he says laughing again, for he has trapped me into responding. "And a just return for thy kind of stubbornness. She shall hold her faith a greater thing than thy flesh; she shall prefer to walk like a peasant rather than be borne like a gentlewoman; she shall scorn satin and lace and cover herself like a winterbound tree earth-hued and hard-barked. And worst of all, she shall have more brains than thee."

"Surely you speak of some afterlife, some penance for a great sin!"

"Na, lad! Thine afterlife is in other hands than mine. 'Tis all thy destiny, lad. Thou may'st not take whatever part of it that pleases thee, and cut the rest to fit thy fancy. The maid will not come here; but should she come here she shall not free thee; but should she free thee, thou wilt indeed finish thy life like a clip-winged hawk, hobbling about amongst the sweating serfs and calling them thine equals."

He reasons right; and fury from inside me pounds my hair-roots. And as the anger mounts, my mind's aswirl again; I seem to be here in this hall with the wizard, yet there, in the dream, in that dusty box of poverty and miracles inhabited by the painter who may not paint. I fight against it, even clinging to this hated hall, holding to the familiar enchantments like Atlantes' hippogriff and unbearable shield, his castle set in everlasting afternoon, and the silent and invisible chains by which he holds me; these, to me, are real, for all they are magic, and not beyond understanding like the painter's chamber with its window overlooking swift horseless chariots, its squat black demon-sculpture which first shrills, then speaks with the voices of people outside the room; its music box no bigger than my two fists, with the glowing golden eye and the sound, sometimes, of a hundred musicians; and all the marvels which are part of his poverty. Again I am he, myself, and he again one, the other, then both, then neither, and again my brains churn in transition. My mouth holds the aftertaste of grapes and mead, then the blue smoke he sucks constantly from his little glowing white sticks; I taste one, the other, both, neither.

I turn from Atlantes and his hated smile and throw myself across the yielding mound of silks and furs. And far away I hear the golden clarion of a bell, the great gong of the castle's magic gate. I hear Atlantes' odd gasp, half surprise, half pleasure; I hear his soft feet on the hard marble. Who comes, who comes a-ringing, challenging, and unwanted—and unafraid of this castle and its many devils? If I am the knight, Rogero, I will watch from the window; if I am Giles, the painter, and I think I am, I will let the goddam doorbell ring. Whoever heard of a doorbell in a magic castle? *What* magic castle?

Here's a dirty bed, and there a dirty window, and over yonder the cleanest canvas yet; now wait, wait—Giles is my name, paint is my trade, if I was a knight, I'd have me a blade. *Give me my sword!*

What sword? Will you for God's sake get away from that doorbell so I can hear myself think? I almost had it then, that business about the knight, whoever he is—or is he *me?*—and his magic mountain, or is that really a furnished room? Ah, *shaddap* with that doorbell already!

"Whaddayewant?"

All it does, it rings.

17

"Who is it?"

Ring, ring.

All right, you asked for it, I'm going to snatch that door open, I'm going to haul off, no questions asked, and punch the nose that's ringing my doorbell. Twist the knob, snatch the door, knock the ringer, to the floor. *Blam,* a dead ringer.

So sometimes a tenth of a second is as long as a paragraph or your arm. The door is open and I'm standing still and tight like a kid looking through a knothole, being with and of the ball game but standing quiet, watching. I watch my hand fly through the door, making a fist on the way, I watch it reach her cheekbone and curl and compact there, pudgy and hard. Back she goes, not falling but standing straight, across the narrow lighted hall and against the wall, *wump-thump!* She is a little brown thing with hair unwonderful, beautiful lashes opening now to make her eyes round and glazed, and that's about all there is to her. "Mmnimmm," she says, and slowly slides down the wall to sit, slowly bends her head to one side, the air ahang like a broken wing. "Well I told you to get away, ringing that bell!" "Mmmm," she breathes.

So I scoop her up, and up she comes, light as a leg o' lamb and common as cabbage, and I kick the door closed and I throw her on the dirty bed, akimbo-crumpled and immodest as a dropped doll, and who cares?—not the artist, who's seen better and wastes no time on the likes of this; not the man, for he is, as the saying goes, not quite himself just now. Here's a dry paint rag to be wet at the sink and wrung out, and pressed against the smooth beige-brown brow over the smooth lids with the tender row of feathers over the seal . . . lashes, I will admit, lashes she has. She has damn-all else but my God! those lashes.

And the rag, coming away, leaves a stain on the brow, verdigris. One can pretend she is a brazen head, skinned with old silk, and the bronze staining through. But only until her eyes open; then there is no pretense, but only a dowdy girl on my bed, a pallor 'pon my unpalatable pallet. She gazes past the green-brown stain and the anger of her brutalized cheek, and she has no fear, but a sadness. "Still nothing?" she murmurs, and I turn and look with her, and it's my empty canvas she is sad for and "Still nothing," half whispering about.

"I am going to punch your face again." It is a faithful promise.

"All right, if you will paint."

"I'll paint or not, whatever I feel like," I am saying in a way that makes my throat hurt. Such a noise it makes, a Day-Glo fluorescent dazzle of a noise. "Giles is my name and paint is my trade, and you keep your nose out of it. Your nose," I say, "looks like a piece of inner tube and you got no more side-silhouette than a Coca-Cola bottle. What you want to be ringing my doorbell for?"

"Can I sit up?"

By which I discover I am hanging over her close, popping and spitting as I bellow and peal. "Get up, get out!" I touch my neck and the scarlet swelling of an artery there, I spin to the easel to strike it but cannot touch it, so go on to the wall and drive my fist against it. It is better than a cheekbone which hardly leaves a mark.

"Oh please, don't hurt yourself. Don't," she says, her voice high and soft-textured around the edges, like light through a hole in worn velvet, "don't!" all pitying, all caring, "don't be angry . . ."

"Angry I am not," I say, and hit the wall again, "angry; I'm a devil and dangerous to boot, so don't boot me. You," I say, pointing at her, and there is blood on my hand, "are a draggletail; bad lines, wrong tone, foreground distracting"—that would be my easel—"background unappetizing." (That would be my bed.) "The whole thing's not composed, it's—it's—decomposed. Where'd you get that awful dress?"

She plucks at it, looks at her hand plucking, makes a faint brief frown, trying to remember. She can't remember, and she is not afraid, she is only trying to answer my question.

"Well don't bother; I don't care where you got the dress. What do you want?"

Up come the lashes. "I want you to paint again."

"Why?"

"Don't, don't," she whispers. "You'll hurt your throat. I know everything you've painted. You're getting good; you're getting great. But you don't paint any more."

"I asked you why; you didn't say why, you just said what happened." She looks at me, still not afraid, still puzzled. This girl, I think, is not only homely, she is stupid. "I asked you why—why? What do *you* care?"

"But I told you!" she cries. "You were going to be great, and you stopped. Isn't that enough?"

"No, not for people. People don't want things like that, greatness, goodness." I begin to be more angry at people than angry at myself. Much better, Giles—*much* better. "People want their work done easily. People want kisses and to feel important. People want to be amused and to be excited safely. People want money. Do you want money? Here's a quarter. Here's forty cents, even. Get out of here, people."

"I don't want money. I just want you to paint again."

"Why?"

Down go the lashes, away goes the voice like a distant wind. "I saw them clustered around your Spanish picture, *Candlelight Malaga*—two young people, holding hands very hard, very quiet; and an old man, smiling; and there was a little boy tugging at a woman's sleeve: 'Ma? Ma?' and when she said, 'Yes, dear,' she kept her eyes on the picture so he cried. I saw a man come away from Garret's, where your *Smoke* was hanging, and he laughed and said to all the strangers, 'All I have to do is *tell* her: she'll love me, it's right there in the picture.' " She spreads her square unwomanly hands to say, "That's what I mean, it's proved."

I don't care about the people, the crying child, the man who speaks to strangers, and all the rest of them. I never painted for them, I painted for—for—but it wasn't for them. So they're all intruders, and for them I've done enough, too much already. If what they have taken was really in the pictures, they have robbed me. If what they took was not there, they are fools. Must I paint for thieves and fools?

All this comes to me clearly, but there is no way to say it to the girl. "It's for those things," she says, as if my silence means I am agreeing with her. "So paint again."

"Paint, how can I paint?"

"Why not? What's the matter?"

"It's my head." I hold it, hard. My elbows knock together; I speak at her, peek at her through the wedge. "I'll tell you because it doesn't make any difference. I'll tell you," I say painfully, "because you don't make any difference." (And oh, no, she wouldn't wince.) "When I painted, I was Giles, Giles yesterday and Giles today, so that where I stopped I could start, and even find the stopping place by tomorrow. And tomorrow I'd be Giles, and knew it so well I never thought about it. Now . . . now I'm Giles. Before that I was—somebody else, and before that I was Giles again. And being Giles now doesn't matter, because soon I'll be someone else again, and after that, Giles. You don't understand that."

"No," she says. "Neither do you."

"Right, so right; the first right thing you've said, no compliments intended, whatever's-your-name."

"Brandt."

"Brandt. *Miss* Brandt, surely, there being limits beyond which the most foolish of men will not go. Painting, Miss Brandt, is a thing having a beginning, a middle, and an end; and the beginning is part of the end of the painting before, and the end is part of the beginning of the next picture. I am Giles, and being Giles I suppose I could paint; but before—an hour or a while ago—say when you were ringing my doorbell, you and your fat nerve—I was somebody else. And soon my brains will scramble and words will mean two things or three, and yonder is either a naked canvas or a far granite wall, and under me a dirty bed or a mound of silks and furs, and what I want will be to paint or to regain my sword; I will be Rogero and Giles, one, the other, both, neither; until suddenly Giles is gone, the easel, the painting—no, not gone, but like a dream, not really remembered because not really real."

"Let Rogero paint," says the fool girl as if she believes me.

There's a noise like one-third of a scream, one-half of a howl, and it's mine. "Rogero paint? He can't paint! He couldn't believe in it, couldn't think it, wouldn't know a tint from a T square. Listen, you; listen to me: can you imagine me as a knight, imprisoned on a magic mountain, surrounded by spells I not only believe in—I *must* because they're real—jailed by a magician who rides a hippogriff? A hippogriff, Miss Unimportant Q. Brandt, you hear? A shining hippogriff whose dam was a brood mare and whose sire was a gryphon—a gryphon whose mother was a lion and whose father was an eagle. This hippogriff is real, real as the spells, real as the magic mountain, real as the knight that you, Miss Interfering W. Brandt, can't imagine me being." (Have I been climbing, running? I am out of breath.) "To that knight," I say when I can, "my telephone and my radio are laughable wonders without foundation in fact, my inability to paint is of no importance except to give me his sympathy; he too is captured and fettered. He can do as little with my brushes as I might do with his sword. And you, Miss Unbeautiful Brandt, could only be the most piddling of small nastinesses intruding into his unbelievable fantasy. Now you know; now I've told you. There's nothing you can do, nothing you can believe, and your coming here or not coming means nothing. If you came to help, you've failed. If you came to fight something, you're beaten."

There is a time for wondering, wondering what someone will say, and this is it, and it is good. Good as anything could be now, where *that* is real or *this* is real, never both. For I lie under a weight and I cannot move it, and when it disappears I am no longer myself, and it is good to defeat someone, something, even an unimportant, unlovely girl; even when in the defeat there can be no victory for me, nor a lessening of the weight. So I wait, wondering in which of several possible ways she will acknowledge her defeat; and here it comes from the usual lips and the eyes behind the unusual lashes; here:

"May I use your phone?"

Because I said she doesn't matter, I may not let this matter either; I step away from the phone and turn my back, and soft footsteps pass me and soft fingers take up the hard phone; there's a chorus of clicks, composed in syncopes, seven measures long. And a ring, and a ring.

What portals open to this lady's ringing, this Brandt for the burning? What dilates to this dialing, this braw, bricht, moonlicht nictitation? My God, my God, here it comes again, the words like lyings in their layers, and I am he, and he is—either or, both, neither. Of these, "or" is king; I wear a coat d'or, that dry, exclusive little word. For we are desiccated to the preposition that all men are created sequels. The "or" is golden but my heart has been read, my mind has been lead; read, lead; just the color of Floradora orange-youth.

"Hello," says the telephone tinily because it can speak two syllables without moving its open mouth; "Giles," says Miss Brandt, "just Giles," and the telephone laughs and says, "Okay."

Soft footsteps on the wooden, or is it marble floor, and the ring has been answered with a shout of laughter; and soft-footed, swift, Atlantes strides to the casement and the curtains of cloud leave the court, the mist melts away from the meadow below, the great golden gate is agleam in the sun, and gone is the gloaming. "Rogero!" he cries (but am I not Giles, imprisoned in a dream, who says he is where a felon needs a friend? *Aiee!* Sharper than a serpent's truth is an ungrateful Giles!) "Rogero, come and see thy destiny!" and in Atlantes' laugh lies such a triumph, such a scorn, I can only come and see. I go to stand beside him.

To either hand are buttresses of weather-hammered stele; before me the castellated wall like a cliff, like a sea becalmed and stood on edge, falls to the courtyard. Away and down and away rolls the magic meadow to its lower margin, mighty walls patrolled by poisoned gnomes. And when I see the gate I am myself again; Rogero, 'prisoned knight, hungering for that craggy path beyond the gate.

"Thy destiny, knight—you see it?"

I look again; and there like a mole under a monument is a small brown person, dun and dowdy. In one hand is a crooked staff little changed from its soil-sprung origins, and it is this which now again strikes the golden bell and sends its clang and hum to shake the shining air. "My destiny?"

He laughs again; there is battle in such laughter. "Look again!" With thumb and finger he makes a circle, and thrusts the hand before my face, and through that circle I see the gate—but not from the mountaintop, but as if I stood but twenty paces away. And though his magic is despicable to me, I yet must look.

Silently, for a long time I gaze. At last I say, "Of all you have told me of my destiny, magician, I see but one thing to bear you out, and that is, that yonder mudball is a maiden, for it is unthinkable that such a one could be anything else. As to the rest, it is not possible that fate should have stored for me anything so . . . unadorned."

"Ah, then thee need only swear fealty to me, and we will squash this beetle together." The bell rings again. "If not, I must do it myself, and keep thee bound as thou art. But one or the other must be done, for that rude clanging is indeed the voice of thy fate, and that barefoot damsel has come as fate dictates, to challenge me and set thee free."

"She challenges *you!*"

"Ay, lad, with nothing but that crooked staff and the home-spun cassock beneath which she generously hides her uninteresting limbs. Oh, and a piddling faith in some unimportant system of gods."

"The staff is enchanted, then."

"No."

"She's mad!"

"She is." He laughs. "So tell me, good fool: wouldst go to her and spend thy days with her, swordless, horseless, tending the plaguey brats of peasants and slaves? Or wouldst thou ride with me and turn her into a damp spot on the meadow, and after, own the earth?"

"I'll choose, wizard, but a choice of mine own devising. I'll not go to her nor ride with you. I shall stay here and watch thy bravery and thine historic victory over that little brown she-monk, with her dried tree-branch arrayed against nothing but thy magic steed, thy mighty armaments, and thine army of gnomes. And when she is vanquished—"

"Thee would see her vanquished?" he mocks. "Thy last chance to be free? Thy destiny contains no other savior."

"When she is vanquished, come back to me that may spit in thy face and tell thee that of my three possible hells, I choose the one which can give thee no pleasure."

He shrugs and turns away from me. At the door he gives me his evil smile. "I knew that one day thee'd call me 'thou,' Rogero."

I snatch up a heavy censer and hurl it. With a crash it stops in midair before him and, broken, falls at his feet. His smile is a laugh now. "Be certain, wizard, that I use not the 'thou' of an intimate, but that of an animal," I roar, and he laughs again; and surely one day, when I find a way, I shall kill this clever creature. I go to the casement.

Far below, I can still see the gate and the shining wall. The gnomes file away and down out of sight; and there, one fragile hand on the golden bars, the other holding the staff, the girl clings peering. Her courage is too foolhardy to be admired and her strength too small to be considered at all; surely Atlantes need only laugh once (that thunder of evil) or raise his brows, to shrivel up this audacious sparrow.

There on the brow of the flying buttress stands Atlantes, the wind whipping his figured mantle, the sun all startled by his jewels.

He raises a hand and turns it, and the gate, so far below, so far away, stands open. Nothing as massive as those golden bars should move so swiftly and noiselessly; the tiny figure at the entrance nearly falls. The girl stands in emptiness, the gate looming about her, the rocky hill behind her, and high and massive over her, Atlantes' castle crowned by the glittering magician himself. She is very small and very alone as she begins to mount the slope.

Atlantes, laughing, claps his hands twice—

And from a copse in the meadow comes a thunder of wings, and a glory. There with an eagle's cruel head and the foreclaws of the mightiest of lions; with the splendid haunches of a stallion and golden hooves—there rises, there floats, there hurtles the hippogriff. His cry ripples the grass; it is a clarion, a roar, and a scream, and through it and through it is a thing which makes my heart melt as never a woman could do, and mine eyes are scalded with pity and fellowship. For he, even he, the hippogriff is enthralled; and with all his soul he hates his master!

I am glad there is no one by, for I weep like a child. I am a knight, and I know my merits; yet everything splendid is behind me. My shackles may not be broken, and my very destiny is without beauty. Yet here before me is beauty crystallized, shaking the world with its piteous, powerful protest . . . crystallized? Nay, alive, alive as a man could never be. See the sun on his golden plumes, oh see his purple flanks . . . he is more than I can bear to look on, to think on . . . I shall have him, mount him!

But if he sees me, knows my heart, I know not, for he sweeps past and hovers, and the top of the buttress takes him like a cupped palm. From the parapet Atlantes takes a curious shield, with its cover of soft bat skins cleverly pieced. He buckles it to the hippogriff's harness, then with a hand on the parapet and a hand on the shield, he climbs to the great beast's back; and oh! I am proud that the steed kneels not for him.

Atlantes leans forward and speaks, and what his word is I may not hear, but the animal's sweet, strong pinions spread and flick the stone but once, and skyward they ride.

In a great circle the hippogriff wheels, with Atlantes leaning from the saddle. His piercing eyes, and all his magic to aid

26

him, must discover any invisible armament she might have; and she must have none, for I hear his distant laughter as he leans over his steed's neck to speak another secret command. The wings go up together and hold like a great wedge, and down they drop just to the height of her head, and with a single thrust and the sound of soft thunder, their speed is checked and they are meadow-borne. Fifty paces away, the girl drops her staff and waits, weaponless.

Tiny and evil, Atlantes' mirth comes to me on the wind. He swings down from the beast's broad back, unbuckles his shield, and with a deft twist casts off its cover.

Now, he stands between me and the girl so that the shield faces away from me. Were it any other way, I should have seen nothing; this I knew when I saw the blaze of light which fanned out and down; when I saw birds swing and flutter and fall, and a stag turn away and blunder into a tree trunk. I had heard of this shield, but until now I had not seen it. In unspeakable ways, its gilded surface had been polished until it struck blind any who saw it. This, then, and the hippogriff, are what Atlantes brings to bear against one girl's fragile madness. Ah, a mighty magician he, and confident.

Beaten and dazzled, she stands frozen, waiting for—no, not mercy; she cannot expect that. Waiting, then, for him.

The work of the shield is done. He covers it and confidently he strides down the slope to her. If he speaks, I cannot hear; I doubt he does, for he knows I am watching, and he will want me to understand. He stoops to pick up the useless staff she has dropped, and thrusts it into her hand; he takes her by the shoulders and turns her about to face the gate; he steps back, then throws up his shaggy head and bellows with laughter. Such dismissal of the blind thing might have been predicted; instant death would have been, for him, too gentle a thing. And so he stands, laughing, impregnable even to such strength as mine, with the invisible wall his spells have built about him; cruel and victorious—ah, a mighty magician indeed!

So, defeated, she moves toward the door . . . door? the gate of gold . . . but no, it is no longer a meadow, but a room where I keep my easel and my . . . and now I see them both, the room and the meadow, as if one were painted upon glass and through it I saw the other; and which? which the painting? *Aiee!* my brains are mixed and muddled again, I am one, the other, both, neither. I see a curtain of sky with mountains for its ragged hem . . . a dirty wall, with one small bright spatter of my blood where I struck it, and the dazed dun maiden raising her staff, which is a small blue book with gold letters on it. "But you're blind!"

Miss Brandt has a twisted smile. Her teeth are no better and no worse than the rest of her, and not to be compared with her lashes. "I've been told that before, but I don't think I am. This is for you—here!" and she gives me the book.

Before or behind my eyes there's a flash, too bright; I think it's a hippogriff. Up here in the salt mines I stand and shiver until the crazy thing passes; I open my eyes slowly and secretively so that I can snatch a reality and make it real. And Miss Brandt is here (or still here, I forget which) and the meadow and the hippogriff become a memory again (or maybe a dream).

"Are you all right?" Her voice and her hand touch me together.

"Stay away from me! I'm crazy, don't you know that?" (Her lashes are up.) "You better get out of here. I'm liable to do practically anything. Look, you're already getting a black eye." I'm yelling again. "Aren't you afraid? Damn you, be afraid!"

"No."

It's a very puzzling thing, the way she should be dressed like a monk, and be holding a crooked stick; but that was a small blue book—that's right. I'm shaking my head, or is it a shudder; the girl and the wall and the door blur by me and my teeth are side-sliding, making a switch-frog sound. It can be halted by holding the heels of the hands on the halves of the head very hard . . . and slowly saliva is swallowed . . . libation, libration, liberation, and quiet at last. In that moment of stillness, when at last I am *here* altogether, I know that my . . . dream, the Rogero thing, whatever it is . . . takes no time at all. For she was at the phone when it began, that last time, and all those things had happened to Rogero while she hung up and took two steps behind me . . . yes, and I heard the steps. So when I become Rogero again, no matter what happens here, how many hours it takes, I shall see Atlantes and the vanquished maid, down and away below, and she fumbling the dry rough stick, blind, defeated destiny of mine.

So open your eyes to here and the easel and Miss Brandt who is not afraid. Hold out the hand with the book. "What's this?"

"Money."

It's a checkbook, sky-green and very disciplined and trackless inside, and sturdy and blue outside. "Blank checks."

"*Cartes blanches.*" She smiles; and this is no place for smiling. So just wait, and the smile will go away. Ah. Unsmiling, she says, "It's money; all you want. Just fill in a check and sign it."

"You're crazy." But she shakes her head gravely.

So: "Why bring me money?"

"You can do whatever you want now."

"I can't paint. Do you think you can make me paint by giving me money?"

When her tongue touches her lips, they are the same color. No one, no woman, should be like that. Such a mouth could taste nothing, take nothing. It says, "Not if you don't want to. But you can do all the other things you want to do—all you have ever wanted to do."

What else have I ever wanted to do but paint? There must be something. Oh, there is, there is; I never had a chance to—to—and then my hand is crushing the book, the book of excellent quality which yields only slightly and, when my hand opens, is bland again. "It's just paper."

"It's money. Don't you believe me? Come with me. Come to the bank. Write out a check and see."

"Money. How much money?"

Again: "All you want." She is so very certain.

"What for?"

"Whatever you like. Anything."

"I didn't mean that." Things are becoming real as real now. "When you take money you give something; you always give something, a painting or a promise or—"

Her head turns briefly, a little, right, left, right, her eyes steady on me, so sliding between the lashes. "Not this money."

"Why are you giving me money?" (You know, Giles, you're frightened?) "What I can do for money mostly is paint. But not now. Not now."

"You don't have to paint. Not unless you want to, and then not for me. Giles, maybe you can't paint because you want to do other things. Well, *do* them. Do them all; finish them until they're all done and there's only one thing left. Maybe then you can work again."

"Then the money's for painting!"

Oh, she is so patient; oh, how I hate anyone as patient as that. "No. It's just for you. Do whatever you want. I don't want the money and I don't ever want it back. It isn't mine to begin with, so why should I care about it?"

"But you'd care if I didn't paint again."

The fringes fall, the lashes hide the ordinary eyes. "I care about that now. I'll always care." And now she has the door open. "Come to the bank. Come get your money. Then you'll believe me."

"The bank, yes, and then what? Go with you, I suppose, and you'll tell me what to buy and where to go and how to—"

"It's yours to do as you please. Now will you come? I'll leave you at the bank if you like."

"I like."

But no, this doesn't hurt her, and no, she is not angry; there's only one thing that touches her, and that one thing reaches through the closed door as we walk in the corridor, stretches down the stairs and past the lintels and the newels and the curbs and cabs and garbage all the way down to the bank; and that one thing is my white, clean, blind square eye of canvas.

I wonder if she knows; I wonder. Wondering under the polyglot columns corralling the bank (Doric they are, with Corinthian capitals, yes but the door is not Doric but arched and Byzantine, closed with a fanlight; I'd say from Virginia). "I wonder if you know."

"If I know what?" she says, still patient.

"Why I can't paint."

"Oh yes," she says, "I know."

"Well I don't, Miss Brandt. I really don't."

"It's because you don't know why you *can* paint," she says, and her eyes are no longer patient, but waiting. It is very different.

And when I shake my head (because that is no answer) her eyes are patient again. "Come," she says; and in we go from the portico, and wouldn't you know the ceiling is red with ropes of gilded plaster draped in altogether Moorish squares.

And here in a low wall made of glazed marble, and flat-topped with marbleized glass, is a little black gate that swings both ways. On the other side is a polished desk and a polished pate bearing polished glasses: "Mr. Saffron," says Miss Brandt; *Mr. Saffron* says the chock-shaped sign on his desk, gold on black.

Mr. Saffron's glittering glasses tilt up; then straight and slowly he rises, like the Lady of the Lake. When he stands, his glasses lose some highlights, and I can see his eyes. They are blue and shiny—not polished, but wet; turned to Miss Brandt they are so round they go pale; turned to me they are slits gone all dark, with a little eave of pink flesh all the way across over both of them. And here is a man who is astonished by Miss Brandt and repelled by me; what a wonderful way he has of showing it, over and over again: round-pale, slit-dark, the whole time.

"This is Giles."

Mr. Saffron gives his slits to my brush-wipe khaki pants, and to my yellow shirt with russet cuffs which is really the top of my ski pajamas, and to my face. "You're quite sure, Miss Brandt?"

"Of course!"

"If you say so," says Mr. Saffron, and sits. "We're quite ready. Will you sign this, Mr. Ahhh?" I hear a drawer move but I am sure he pulls the white card from his spotless stomach. With the shiny pen from his desk set I write *Giles.*

"First name?" says Mr. Saffron to the card, another shiny pen in hand.

"Yes."

"Last name?"

"Yes," I say again; and up come the glasses. "That's his name, just Giles," Miss Brandt says quickly. And then she recites my address. Mr. Saffron writes it, putting no more of his boiled-veal fingers on the card than he has to.

Miss Brandt says, "You want to cash a check now?"

"Oh sure." I fumble around and get the book. Miss Brandt comes close with a finger. "You write the date there, and the—" But I just sit there looking up at her until she goes away. What's the matter, does she think I don't know how to write a check? I write the check.

Mr. Saffron takes the check by its two ends and it flips softly like a little trampolin. He turns it over with a brittle snap and does a squiggle with his pen. "Sixty-eight dollars. All right, the cashier will give you your money." From his drawer he takes a yellow, ruled pad and curls down over it as if there were sudden fire in his watch pocket. Out we go through the little black gate, and when I look back he is not busy with his paper at all, but staring after us the round-pale way.

"Is that all you want—sixty-eight dollars?"

I look at her. "What would I do with more than sixty-eight dollars?"

Patient, patient she says, "Anything, Giles. *Anything.*"

So we go to a cage and a fierce face says in a sweet voice,

32

"How do you want it?"

"Cash."

"Any way at all," says Miss Brandt.

So he gives me the money and we go to a marble table in the middle of the bank while I look at it. Miss Brandt says, "Is that right?"

"What?"

"Is it all there? Weren't you counting it?"

"Oh no. I was just looking at it. It really is real money."

"I told you."

"Is there more?"

Again she says, "All you want."

"Okay, good. Well, Miss Brandt, you can stay here or go do whatever you want."

"All right."

I walk away and when I get to the big door with the fanlight I look back. Miss Brandt is standing there by the table, not exactly looking my way. I come walking back. I have a feeling inside that makes the base of my nose hurt. I stop by her and look at her while I wet my lips. She has a real sunset of a shiner by now but the lashes are all right. So I tell her, "You just don't care what happens to me now."

"You know I do."

"Well, why didn't you try to stop me if you cared so much?"

She says, "You're not going to do anything important just now."

"With all this money? How do you know?"

She doesn't say.

"I guess you want me to come running back to you so you can take care of me."

"No, Giles, truly," she says in that absolutely certain way. "You don't understand. I'm not important. I'm not trying to be important. I just don't matter in any of this."

"Not to me." Why does she make me so mad anyway? "So what *is* important?"

"Why you could paint. Why you can't paint. That's all."

"Well, the hell with that for now. Well—maybe I'll see you around."

She sort of shrugs. I just go. Maybe I want to turn around but I don't. There's something in my head about how do I get in touch with her if I should want to, but the hell with that too.

By all the paint pots of perdition, nobody's ever going to make Giles admit he's a part of the works, like she does. People like her, all they do is go around believing in something and trying to trap other people into believing it too. "I just don't matter in any of this." What kind of a way to get along is that, the silly bitch?

I get out of line of the bank door and then go across the street and stand in a low areaway where I can watch her when she comes out. From now on by God my business is *my* business. Who does she think she's brushing off?

It's getting chilly out, but who cares? I've got lots of time. Lots of money. Lots of patience. Miss Brandt, now, she's *really* got patience. On the other hand, all God's chillun got patience. Will you look at that bank, now; those big fat pillars are doing just what? Holding up a pseudo-Parthenonic frieze, that's what. That's really patience. Year in, year out they stand there holding it up and nobody knows it's there but the starlings. Patience—look at the work that went into carving all those figures, that fat, baggy nude in the middle clear down to the chow dogs or lions or whatever they are at the ends. *Stiacciato,* they call that work, the lowest form of relief, and that fat one in the center, she sure would be. So they in turn are patient, the hodgepodge of Hermes and Demeters and blind Justices, holding still for the starlings. And when it's cold the starlings freeze on the marble stool, and when it's warm they stool on the marble frieze, and the meek shall inhibit the earth.

Oh holy Pete what's happening to my head . . . listen, Giles, hold on to this area rail and keep your wall eyes on that bank and don't go off into no magic mountains. Watch that clock over the door. Watch it? I can *hear* it! Well listen to it then

34

and keep your head in the here and now and don't let yourself go splitting the definitive. That, now, is a sick clock, it must be three hours slow, and listen to it moan. Oh I know a bank where the wild time groans . . . Hang on, Giles boy; think of something else, like San Francisco where the second-story men from across the Bay are called berkelers, and the Golden G—no! Think of the statue down the block, the Mayor's father on a horse, that's in the papers every other day should they move it or not . . . My father's horse has many mentions . . . and in the bank, now, Miss Brandt is leaving, see the gate is open and agleam in the sun as she stumbles on stones; it is as if Atlantes' mirth alone were bending her down to be crushed like a tree in a thunder-wind. And across the street—but meadow, meadow's the word—the blue-black helmets of the beastly gnomes show as they watch this . . . could it be called a challenge? Ay; but a battle, no; only a defeat.

All this in a flash of stern anger, and then—yea, she is sinking, twisting about as if to fall at his feet . . . then up she comes in a whirl, her crude staff invisible, lost in speed, and with a whip's crack, the staff . . . *Aiee!*

For a moment I cling to the casement, scrabbling like a cat half-fallen from a wall; in that incredible moment I have leaned forward to shout and have all but pitched out through the window; and what of my destiny then?

Back at last and looking outward:

And the gate is lead, and shrunken, and the gnomes but a herd of goats; I stand not on a mighty parapet, but on the roof of a byre. Bone are the swan pools, the great gray halls, the soft-footed dancers and the grape-girls. Atlantes, mighty Atlantes, lies on his back with his eyes glazed and the bright blood flowing from his broken head . . . lying, *aiee!* like a goatherd after a bottle-fight on market day. And his steed— but horror itself! has she then turned the hippogriff into a milch cow? May the mandrake curdle her bowels if she's harmed my hippogriff!

Ah but no; there he stands, the blazing beauty, and throws

back his eagle's head, and hurls his joy away to the farthest mountains. I mingle my shout with his, leap free of the wall, and run and tumble down the meadow.

In a transport I stretch myself against the unenchanted grass, and twist and turn in it until I can smell its sweet green ichor; and in just such a turning mine eyes fall upon her who stands meekly by, her two hands folded about the piece of her broken staff, her eyes downcast—but not so far they see me not.

"But 'tis thee, my warrior-maid!" I roar. "Here to me lass, and I'll buss thee well for thy trouble!"

But she stands where she is, so I must go to her. That at least I can do; has she not set me free?

(Or is she here to imprison me again? Destiny, now, is not fragile; yonder's a fractured magician for proof. Still—) "How do they call thee, maid?"

"Bradamante," says she; now, the Arabs breed a long-maned horse, and in the distance that silken banner on their necks looks like this maid's lashes close to.

"Well, Bradamante, I owe thee my freedom if not my life. And should I pay the reckoning, what would thee do with them?"

Up to me she looks, with a deep calm which destroys my reckless smile; and up past me she looks further; and she says gently, "I would do the Lord's will with them."

"Call me not Lord!" I cry; this creature embarrasses me.

"I did not." Quiet as ever, her voice, yet somehow she chides me. "I meant the Lord Whom I serve, Who is King of kings."

"Is He now! And what would He have thee do with a belly-hungry, prison-broke hellion of a swordless knight?"

"If thou wilt serve Him—"

"Hold, lass. Yon wizard told me a tale of thee and me betrothed, and crawling the mud like worms among worms with never a jewel to our cloaks. He said 'twas my destiny to be freed by thee, and free me thee did. Though I can't say how."

36

"I but struck him with my staff."

"Na, lass. Even I could never do that; he could not be touched."

She gives me her hand; I take it and then follow her gaze to it. It wears a simple golden ring. Gently she frees herself and removes the ring. "The Lord sent this my way; who wears it is proof against all enchantments. I need it no longer." The ring flashes in the sun as she casts it aside; with my quick thumb and forefinger I pluck it out of the air.

"But keep it, Bradamante! Thee cannot discard such a treasure!"

"It was given me to free thee, and thou art free. As to the future—the Lord will provide."

I slip the ring upon my smallest finger, and though it is thick as her thumb, the ring clasps me like mine own. (Even without it, girl, thee'd have better fortune with an angry basilisk than thee would with me, if thee would persuade me to join thee on thy rocky pilgrimages. But now—) "This much of my destiny is complete, then, Bradamante, and I am in thy debt. But surely the wizard was wrong about the rest of it."

"It is in the hands of the Lord."

"Thee doesn't expect me to cast aside my brocades for a scratchy gown like thine, and go with thee among the peasants!"

"We do as the Lord directs. We do it freely and with all our hearts, and are saved, or we do it blindly until we end in darkness; but serve Him we shall."

Such confidence is more unnerving than any magic. "I cannot believe that."

"*Will* not," she corrects me calmly.

"But I've choice! Here we stand, Bradamante, and in the next heartbeat I might slay thee or woo thee or bite thee or fall on the earth and gobble grass; and which of these things I do is for me to decide!"

Slowly and so surely she shakes her head. "It is in thee to

serve the Lord, else I should not have been sent to thee. Choice thee has: Thee may serve Him willingly or thee may serve Him blindly; and none has a third way."

"Thee cannot force—"

She puts up her hands. "We do not force. We do not kill. We need not. The Lord—"

"Thy Lord let thee kill Atlantes!"

"No, Rogero. He is not dead."

I spring to the crumpled magician; and indeed, he is but stunned. I snatch out his own poiniard, and instantly, under its point, Bradamante thrusts her firm brown arm. "The Lord will take him in his own time, Rogero. Spare him."

"Spare him! He would have killed thee!"

"But he did not. He too is a servant of God, though unwilling. Spare him."

I fling down the blade so violently that nought but the jeweled knob at the hilt-top shows between the grass-blades. "Then I will; and having done thee the one service, I shall call my debts discharged. Art satisfied, girl?"

She makes my head bubble, this quiet creature; and I recall Atlantes' scoffing words, that this dedicated beetle of a Bradamante shall think more of her faith than of my flesh, and that she shall have more brains than I.

Her lashes fall, and "Sobeit," she says, and not another word.

I need my sword, and to get it I must turn my back on her—a good need. So up the slope I go lightly, just as if her very presence were not like a heat on my shoulder blades. I close my eyes as I spring up the smooth grassway, and it does nothing to shut her out.

Patience, Rogero! Down the hill, over the rise, and she'll be forgotten!

And in any case, one could come back if one must . . . .

So I let my eyes come open again, and gasp; for there stands the hippogriff, and he has never let me come so close. If I am to continue upward I must go round him, or I must move him. For a split second I falter, and his great head comes round to me; and oh, I've looked in the wells of Kazipon which are bottomless, I've followed the light of my torch in the endless caverns of Qual, and I've known a night when the stars went out; and never before have I looked into such depths and such reaches as the eyes in his eagle head. True bird's eyes they are, fierce in their very structure and unreadable. Through them the beast sees—what? A soft sac of blood and bones to be a sheath for that golden beak . . . or a friend . . . or a passing insect . . . I should flee. I should stand. I should sidle about him and be wary. I should, I should—

But I shall ride him!

I finish my stride and go straight to him, and when my hand falls on his purple shoulder he swings his head forward and high, and trembles so that from his wings comes a sound like soft rain on a silken tent. My heart leaps so that I must leap with it or lose it, and with a single motion I am on his back and my knees have him. *Aiee!* such a shout comes from me, it would rival his own; it is full of the joyous taste of terror. With it I fetch him a buffet on the withers which jars me to the very neckbones, and before I can feel the blow as any more than a shock, his wings are open and thrusting, and he rears and *leaps . . . .*

It is a leap that never will end; fast he flies and faster hurtling higher just at the angle of his leap, and the surges of his body are most strange to a horseman. Only the glint of the golden ring convinces me that we are not involved in an enchantment; for flying sunward warms nothing, curious as it may seem, and the bright air grows cold as the hoary hinges of perdition's door.

I think of poor sod-shackled Bradamante, and look back and down; but by now she is lost in that indeterminate new place between haze and horizon, and there, for all of me, she may stay. I shrug, and find that I have not shrugged away the picture of her face, which is strange, since it is hardly one worth remembering. Surely, Rogero, thou art not smitten?

With her? With—*that?*

Ah no, it could not be. There must be something else,

something buried in the whole mosaic of our meeting. Of our parting . . . ah; that was it!

Atlantes is not dead.

That in itself is nothing; Atlantes distant is, to me, as good as Atlantes dead. But Atlantes slowly waking in the meadow, his enchantments all destroyed, his shield and steed gone—and the peaceful author of his ruin doubtless helping him to his feet with her sturdy unwomanly hands . . . this is another matter.

But forget it! The sly-tongued termagant could, by the time Atlantes was fully conscious, have him so morassed in debate he would forget to be angry. Bradamante has a most powerful helplessness; she attacks with the irresistible weapon of being unarmed, immobilizes the enemy by surrendering, and at last sits on his feeble form, holding by the great weight of her passivity. I need not fear for Bradamante.

But the ring flicks a mote of light into mine eye, and I know I have taken her last defense and left her at the mercy of the merciless, and this is small thanks indeed for what she dared for me.

But what else would a knight, a true knight, do?

One thing a knight would do, I tell myself bitterly, is to regain his sword if he lost it, and not pleasure himself with a hippogriff, however beautiful. Thou art no knight, Rogero; not yet, not again. Regain thine own holy blade, its very hilt encrusted with thy sacred promises, ere thee call thyself knight again.

Back, then, for the sword, and decide then about the maiden; and keep thyself armed with the thought of thy destiny—it is with her, and means soaking in meekness until I am mushy as bread in a milk bowl . . . *no!* by the heart of the fire in the nethermost pit, I shall get my blade and hew out a new destiny!

There are no reins, and I remember that the magician controlled the beast with words. "Enough, my beauty!" I cry. "Back now—take me back!" And somewhere inside a voice sniggers *Thee deludes thyself with the matter of the sword; it's the plight of the maid that drives thee.* "No!" I cry, "she shall not have me! Let her King of kings save her, she's His ward, not mine!" And I thump the hippogriff with my hard-tooled heels: "Back, my beauty, take me back!"

And the hippogriff tilts to the wind, and balances and sails as before, for these are not the magic words.

"Turn! Turn!" I bellow, roweling him. I ball my fist and sink half of it in the feathered root of his neck just forward of the shoulder; for by this, if rightly done, one may stagger a horse. "Mule!" I shriek. "Turn thy spavined carcass about ere I tie a knot in thy neck!"

At this the eagle's head turns about like an owl's and the measureless eyes loom over me. Slowly the beak opens that I may see the spear tip and the scissor sides of that frightful weapon. Like a blind animal, the gray-pink tongue shifts and searches and settles again; the tongue itself is adversary enough for any soldier. Fear, however, is an assistant to safety only up to a point, and I am far past it. "Go back, aborted monster, ere I snatch out that ugly horn and crack thine eyeballs together! By the pleasure-bred blood of thy half-bred dam and the—" Thus far I rant, and he strikes. And would he had killed with the one stroke; for instead he has slipped the point of his beak between my saddle and my hams, and I am flipped, unharmed and sore humiliated, high in the air over him. I am spinning like a broken lance, or the earth is circling me head to heel, chased by a blazing band of sun. I see the glory-tinted wings below me, too small and far away; around I go and see them again closer; and again, and this time I must touch, clutch; I claw my hands and flex my legs, and turn again—and the hippogriff slips away to the side to let me plunge past him.

I cover my eyes and I scream; I scream till my tendons cannot bear it, sob and scream again fit to startle the starlings off every bank from here to Brookline, Mass. I recant, I'll accept my destiny and honestly wed the little brown nun, if

she'll have me; ay, and do for her Lord what paltry dog-tricks
He'll ask of me; only make this hippogriff, this lovely,
legitimate, honorable beauty of a hippogriff save me. *Aiee!*
and I'll lie on my back on a scaffold and paint Thee murals,
Lord, and I swear never to punch Miss Brandt in the eye, or
anywhere else again, if thee'll but send me a cloud or an eagle
or a parachute or a helicopter . . . oh holy Pete, what a spot
for him to lose his mind in and be me again. I wonder if he
knows it won't take any real time at all, where he is. And
there below me the mottled earth pursues a sun-turned-rock-
et . . . whew. Giles old boy, don't you shut your eyes again
until you have to— "Hullo!"

There at the area railing stands a smut-faced urchin and a
smaller but female version of himself, all eyeballs and streaky
cheeks. "Gee, mister, you all right? You sick?" and the
smaller one: "Canchasee, he's *dyne!*"

"Don't mind me, kids," I mumble. "I just fell off a
hippogriff." I find I'm half-kneeling and try to stand, and it
seems my hands are locked around the iron uprights of the
railing. I stay there stooped and feeling very foolish while
they watch me, and I concentrate from my stone-cold
marrow up and out until at last my left fingers begin to stir.
With a little more effort the hand comes free, and with it I
disengage the right, one finger at a time. I straighten up then
and look a while at my hands and wiggle them. "He ain't
dyne," says the boy in a robbed tone, and his cohort says
defensively, "Anyway, he *wuz* dyne," because her ardent
hopes had made it her production.

Briefly, a sun flashes past, but I ignore it; I'll be all right
now. You get so you know the signs. "Here," I say, "I'll try
to do better next time," and I give them money, I don't
know how much but it must be enough; they beat it.

I put my elbows on the railing, keeping these spastic hands
away from it, and look across the street. The clock hands
haven't moved any that I can see, and Miss Brandt, who was
just starting out the door when my addled brains caught up
with me, is pausing on the portico, the door just closing

42

behind her. Two seconds, three maybe. My God, what a way to live!

Miss Brandt looks up the street and down, descends the shallow steps and turns right toward the old Mayor's statue. When she has quite gone I cross to the bank and go inside. At the island table I write a check, and take it to the wicket where the fierce-faced man is caged. He takes the paper and turns it over with the same snap Mr. Saffron used, and that is a trick I must learn one day. "You'll need to get this initialed," he says. So off I go to Mr. Saffron again, and stand in front of his shiny desk until he looks up at me and makes the pink meaty ridge across and above his narrowed eyes. The man disapproves of me to the point of ecstasy, and I take this as a kindness; for it makes us both feel important. I let the check fall to him, and he looks, snaps, looks, and grunts. "All right, Mr. Ahh," he says, and squiggles on it with his personal pen. I take the check and stand where I am.

"Well?"

"I want to know whose money this is."

"Yours." He has a way of snapping off the margins of his words as if he doesn't want you to have a whole one.

"Yes, but—"

"The deposit is in your name; surely that's sufficient!"

I look at the check. "Is there any more left?"

He is offended by the whole thing, but he is stuck with it. "There is," he says.

"Much?"

"More than you can spend today," he says. "Or this week."

"Well, dammit, how *much?*"

He sort of spreads his pale-pink hands, which means, I gather, that this is not an account like other accounts and he wishes he could do something about the irregularity but he can't. He says, "That is the one and final checkbook you get. Aside from that, there doesn't seem to—ahh—be any upper limit. And now you'll excuse me, I've a great deal to good day Mr. Mmmm." And down he goes to his papers.

Well, I've asked enough questions to know there won't be

any answers. I go back to the wicket and slide the fierce one
the check. "Half in hundreds and the rest in small bills." He
makes a long snort or a short sigh, clicks the bars between us
down tight, lets himself out the back with a key, and is gone
for too long, but I don't mind about that just now. Pretty
soon he's back with a sack. He opens the wicket and starts
taking stacks out of the sack and sliding them to me. The
sixty hundreds go into my socks; they have elastic tops and
pull up high enough. The sixty fifties fan out flat enough to
go between my belly and my knit shorts, though they hump
up some. Then I spend some time with the hundred and
eighty twenties and tens, cramming 'em into two side and
one back pants pocket. By now I'm lumpy as a sofa cushion
just out of the wet wash and I've collected quite a crowd.
The fierce face flutes, "You're going to run into trouble,
carrying all that money that way," as if it was a wish, and I
say "No I won't. They all think I'm crazy, and there's no
telling what a crazy man will do." I say it good and loud, and
all the people watching stop their buzz-buzz and back off a
little. They make a wide empty aisle for me when I start
away.

"Wait!" cries the teller, and punches some keys on his little
machine. Coins slide down the half-spiral chute and pile up in
the cup at the bottom with a cast-iron clink. "Wait! Here's
your twenty-eight cents!"

"Keep it!" I bellow from the door, and go out feeling a lot
happier than I've been feeling lately. All my life I've wanted
to leave twenty-eight cents for a bank teller, who wouldn't
put it in his pocket to save his soul, and who hasn't got any
place for it in his books.

Down the street there's a big men's shop with little letters
over the door and a windowful of somber-colored suits with
no creases in the jacket arms. I look them over until I find
the one with the most pockets and then I go inside.

It's like a church in there, but with wall-to-wall broadloom,
and the only showcases I can see are two little ones set into

mahogany pillars, one with tie-clasps and collar pins, one with four hand-painted silk ties. I go look at the first one. Every velvet box has a humble little card with "the" on it: *$200 the set; $850 the pair.* I'm on my way to look at the ties when a tall man with a paper carnation steps out of a potted palm and stands where I have to run him down in case I'm not going to stop.

"What," he says, "do you want?" The "you" is a little bigger than the other words and the whole thing sounds like he's pretty disgusted. I tell him about the suit in the window.

He laughs with his mouth. "That is a three-hundred-dollar suit."

"Well, drag it on out."

"I'm rawtha sure we don't carry your size," he says, looking at my painting pants.

"Then we'll hack it till it fits," I tell him. "Come on, buster, quit stalling."

"I'm afraid that—"

So I start yelling a little, and he backs off and bleats "Mr. Triggle, Mr. *Trigg*le!" and from somewhere—I guess another potted palm, there's plenty around—comes another tall man in the same sort of funeral suit, but this one's got a real carnation. "Here," he says, "here-here-here. What's this, what?"

"You're selling, I'm buying. Only he don't think so," I tell the real carnation, pointing at the paper one.

The paper one says, "The gentleman"—dirtiest word I ever heard, the way he says it—"the gentleman is inquiring after the von Hochmann worsted in the window."

The real carnation nickers. "My good man, I'm afraid you've come to the wrong—" and then I put twenty dollars in his hand. He looks at it and the other one looks at it so I give him one too. They look at each other, so I pass out two more. "Get the suit."

"Won't you step into the sample room?" says the real carnation, and you wouldn't know it was the same man. It

45

certainly isn't the same voice. "We have quite a selection in—"

"I don't want a selection, I want that suit in the window. That very goddam selfsame suit and not one like it."

"Oh but we can't get a suit out of the—" So I give them each twenty dollars. "Yes, *sir!*" says the paper one, and dives to the front.

"Now let's see," says the real carnation, pulling at his chin and trying to imagine me with my face washed. "Once we get the suit out of the way, we'll look at some cravats, and perhaps an English broadcloth, hmmm? Handmade? Rolled collar, studs? Yes indeedy."

"No indeedy. I got a shirt." I pluck at the yellow ski pajama top. This shuts him up without any money changing hands.

The other tall man comes back with the suit and we parade into the fitting room which looks more than ever like part of a funeral home, only bigger. The two of them stand in the middle of the room wringing or rubbing their hands while I step into a curtained booth and put the suit on. The pants got no cuffs yet and the coat's too tight. I come out and they jump all over me like Hansel and Gretel on the gingerbread house. When they get to measuring the pants they find out I still got my old ones on underneath. Forty dollars fixes that up too, before they can say anything.

So when they're finished chalking and pinning they want to know when I want the suit. "Now!" I roar, and before either of them can so much as "But we—" I give them money again. "How many people you got back in there, altering?"

"Eight, sir."

"Well, here." I give him eight twenties. "Give 'em this and put 'em all to work on this one suit. You've got nine minutes."

"Yes, *sir,*" and off goes paper carnation, breathing hard.

The other one says, "You said you were in the movie line?"

"I did not."

"Ahh," he says. "Oil."

"Nup. Ladies' wear. I put out a line of underskirts with prints of umbrellas and telephones on 'em. You've seen 'em."

"I—ahh—don't know that I have."

"*What?*" I shout, "You never heard of a Freudian slip?"

"Why, I—" and after that he shuts up. He keeps looking at me.

They don't get the suit ready in nine minutes but they make it in eleven. As soon as the man shows with the suit over his arm, I tell him, "Hey, I forgot. I want the left sleeve three-eights of an inch shorter than the right one." His jaw drops, but the real carnation says "Do it, Hopkinson." And the other one goes out with the suit, me diving along right behind him. We get to a door about the same time. Inside is a real patchy workroom with bright lights and racks of suits, two old women and six old men. "But sir, you can't—"

"Shut up and give me that," I say, and snatch the suit. "I didn't want the sleeve fixed, I just wanted to see these people. Listen," I say to the whole room, "did he give you any money just now, this guy with the paper flower?"

All those old people stand and blink at me till somebody says "Money?" and then they all shrug their shoulders and wag their heads. Paper flower, all nods and smiles, steps forward and says, "Why, I was going to give it to them just as soon as the suit was satisfactory," and he takes the eight twenties out of his side pocket. I bang them out of his hand and stick them into my pants. "You were like hell, you crumb." I go down into my sock and haul out the pack of hundreds and go around the room giving one to each of the old people. The real carnation sticks his head in just then and I tell him, "You better get that guy out of my sight before something happens around here even my money won't fix." The paper flower disappears.

I go back to the booth and this time I take off the old pants. I spread the money around through all the pockets in the suit—it's got fourteen—and get dressed. I give the carnation three hundred dollars and my old pants. "You keep 'em. They should fit pretty good." I have to admire him; I can see he's all aquiver inside, but he still walks like a bishop at a coronation as we go to the door, and as he walks he's carefully folding my old pants, which hasn't happened since I brought them home from Kresge's two years ago, until they hang flat as an antimaccassar over his forearm. He opens the door for me and by God, *bows.* "Thank you *so* much, and come back to us soon, Mr. Freud."

It's close to nighttime, eating time. Around the corner and up the street is a restaurant I've heard about that used to be a stable. I'm just pushing through the door when in front of me there grows a soft wall made of maroon serge and brass buttons and a monstrous braided golden silk rope. I step back and look up, and it isn't a wall, but the prow of a commodore-type doorman; and I swear he's eight feet tall before the hat starts.

"Sorry, sir; you can't go in like that."

The suit, it seems, gets me a "sir" but not any courtesy in the voice. "Like what?"

He puts up a hand like a punching bag and taps himself on the Adam's apple. I put up my hand and touch only my yellow ski-pajama top. "Oh, the tie," I say.

"Oh," he says, "the tie." Mimicking somebody like that, now that's for murder; that's worse than what Rogero called the hippogriff. "Well, you didn't happen to notice I got no tie."

He pushes out his chest. It looms up and over me like the business end of a hydraulic forging press. "I did happen to notice you got no tie," he says, still copying my voice and you know? He's pretty good at it.

"You did, for sure?" I say, and give him twenty dollars.

"Well, kind of one-eyed I did," he says in a new voice which wasn't mine and wasn't the "sir" voice I first heard, but one which seems to come easiest of all to him. I give him another twenty, and he lets me go on in.

A man meets me at the inner door—quite a man, boiled shirt, tailcoat, and the magnificent head you see in college lobbies, the oil painting of the previous Dean. With one flick of his eyes—and mind you, the light's not too good just there—he does with me what Mr. Saffron does with a check; he reads me, turns me over with a snap, puts his squiggle on me so that the inside man will do what's absolutely correct. It must be a problem, with the new suit and the worn shoes and the dirty face and the fact that the doorman let me in; but if it bothers him he doesn't show it. "Good evening, sir," he says. His tone has the depth of one of those console radios they built in the thirties, when the more money you had, the more bass you bumped your belly with. "Step right this way."

But I knock his elbow. "It bothers you I got no necktie."

"Why—no, sir."

"Yes it does." I take out a hundred-dollar bill and fold it lengthwise and pleat it good and tight, and then I take a fifty and fold it flat and narrow, and wind it once around the middle of the hundred. Then I take the two pleated ends and spread them so I have a bow, tied in the middle. He stands there waiting for me as if people did this kind of thing all the time. "Now lend me the pin off that flower of yours." He hands it to me, carrying it the last half inch of the way by a subtle and courteous bow from the waist. I pin the bow to the front of my yellow ski-pajama top. "A tie. Okay with you?"

"Quite suitable, sir."

"I thought you'd like it." I pull it off and hand it to him. "I want a table for eight on the edge of the floor."

"Yes, sir. I have just the one." Off he goes, and me after him, and sure enough, there's a big round table. He plucks a subdued ivory *Reserved* card off it and sits me down. "And when do you expect the rest of your party?"

"I'm the rest of the party."

"Very good, sir. And you're drinking—"

"Brandy. Double. The kind that nobody but you knows is the best in the place."

"I have just the year. Water? Soda?"

"Yoghurt," I say. "About half-and-half."

"Right away, sir."

49

So I have that and a liver-and-oatmeal sandwich and crepes Suzettes with a jubilee sauce made (by four men with three shiny carts) with those little tiny wild French strawberries, and you know? It costs eighty-four bucks to eat in that place.

I sit and I watch the show, and I watch the watchers watching the show. And I plan the things I shall do with more money than I can spend. I shall leave here when it is too late to hire anything and I'll make my money rent a powerboat. I'll leave twice the price with the owner and I'll sink it, and never be seen again by him, so he'll wonder. I'll buy two islands with two mansions, and on one I'll pretend to be a prude while through an agent I'll lease everything but my house to nudists; and the other island I'll populate with prudes while I go naked. I'll buy Thomas Moore's own harp from the Institute and build in a contact microphone and a music box which will play "Red Wing" for forty minutes at double tempo if anyone touches it. I'll train up a man who can fascinate as many hungry people as Huey Long and as many frightened people as Joe McCarthy, both at the same time, and when he takes over he'll pull a switch on them all and be as gentle and as poor and as strong as Jesus of Nazareth. And I'll supply every male teen-ager with a hand-tainted pie, and every female with a totally new orgasmic term to apply to sundaes, convertibles, knobby-faced pop vocalists and shoe straps. For Bradamante a transparent lipstick so she can feel like a woman even if she doesn't want it to show, and for Atlantes (poor little rich man) the full realization of destiny's indestructibility.

Look yonder: look! There by herself, with a candle on her table, sits the most beautiful woman who ever lived. Her hair is soft sable, long, straight, fine, and thick; her eyes and cheekbones the delicate strong interacting Eurasian arch-sequence. Her nostrils are petal-textured, moving as indetectably as the shift from one aurora-pattern to the next, but sensitively in motion even from her shallow breathing as she sits still, so still . . . and surely she is the saddest woman who ever lived, or a mouth such as hers could not be sleeping so, nor the head turned and held just that way of all ways, nor the shoulders so careless and the hands so forgotten. Is she grieving from loneliness, in the knowledge that never in life can she meet her like? Or has she been hurt by a small someone, and cannot understand?

I raise a hand, and the Dean-faced obsolescent console drifts to me. "Who is she?"

"I'll find out for you in a moment, sir."

"No, don't!" It bursts from me. "Please don't." (Now, why not?) "You mustn't do that."

"Very well, sir," and as if he senses my distress, "really I won't."

"Why is she so sad?" And I don't know I've spoken until he answers: "I think she has been disappointed, sir. She has been sitting there alone for a long while." He bends a little closer, as if to add a great importance to what he has to say. "I think, sir, that she is very young."

And somehow I understand precisely what he means; he means that she is frightened, but will not suggest fear in the burnished security of this moneyed place, of which he is such a piece.

Fear . . . there are fears and fears, depending upon one's origins and sense of value. Seimel, who hunts tigers with a spear, faces death without fear, and I know a man who is struck numb at the sound of a key in a Yale lock; who's to say which terror is great or small, or that it's a small thing to be a girl who dares not leave a table because she has no money? "Well, let her go. I'll take her check."

"Yes, sir." His glossy finish emits, like an alpha particle, a brief bright flash of approval. "Shall I take her your card?"

"Oh God no!" Again the thought of knowing her at all distresses me. "Just say a hippogriff flew by."

Unperturbed he says, "Quite, sir," and, as a good piece of furniture should, rolls silently and unbendingly away on his casters.

I wait, and I wait; and there coming in is a chinchilla coat which will be flung over a chair somewhere just under a light, and yonder a fat face laughs too loudly; the trombone, part of a chord, still gives me two notes exactly right for a girl's inexpressible loneliness and my feelings about it, and the man with the shiny cart moves the heel of a silver spoon deftly through the pure transparent heat springing bluely from the bubbling blood of the jubilee . . . and as if by accident, the fine Dean's head bows over the girl's table and he speaks to her.

Her face, when she looks up, blinds me for a moment. Or maybe my tears do. She radiates no happiness—some great grief is bred too deeply into this girl's fine bones—but there is a change which permits hands to be remembered and a mouth to live again. It could have been fear and its removal, an excision which works wonders with dogs and humans, and might, I imagine, even with nations.

And so she may turn her head away from sorrow, and when she does, the breath catches in my throat; in the nocturnal texture of her hair lies a single streak of silver, a hue of just the deadness, just the distance of a winter moon. No other color could treat with such precision of an inherent sorrow, and no other creature has been so correctly branded as this girl.

I saw motion pictures of a lily growing; shoot to blossom in a brace of seconds; and as it rose and burst, so she rises and shakes back her hair. I saw a strand of spider web drift by and away, streaming; and so she passes. I saw a bird die in the hollow of my hand, its open crystal eyes unchanging; and so I sit now unchanged, except that something is gone out of me.

I shall invoke Rogero, and escape from this tomb into terror; I shall not wait for a summons to his world. Better to be falling away through a shining sky with angry wings above me and a sudden quiet below, than to sit here in the meshes of my several madnesses. Insanity is only wisdom of a sort, too deeply driven for the sphincters of the mind to compass; and this is the riddle of the sphinx. Brushless Giles, the ex-painter, is (when you come right down to it) a far wiser person than Swordless Rogero, ex-knight. Put me on a hippogriff without a driver's license and I won't sit and bawl "Back, sir!"; I'll push the buttons and pull the levers and watch what happens until I can back into anybody's downhill driveway. And if words are the reins, the throttle, and clutch, then words I'll try, until at last I have a "Gee" for him and a "Haw" for him and above all a big fat "Whoa!" Rogero, now, he's a fool, and rather healthier than I and therefore more alive; his uncertainties are a little less well-founded in fact than mine. *Whoosh!* and is that the hot, gentle ignition of brandy over yonder, or the sun passing my feet? Is that polite patter halfhearted applause for the band or is it the wind in the wings of the wheeling beast above me? Catch me, catch me, good knight and I shall die gladly with thee, free of both these insupportable worlds. But I am not falling; I hang here in dusk, supported by a rushing wind, a central point for the looming earth and the hurtling sun as they rotate about me. (And if hanging thou art, why are the crags of Earth larger each time they pass thee?) *Aiee,* could I but die of foolhardiness, like a Bradamante challenging the powers of evil, and not thus crotch-flung in penance for the silly vapors of my foul mouth, not humiliated and screaming like a whipped serf. (Waiter, bring me an orchestra playing Rampart Street, I have fallen from Grace, who is a hippogriff.)

Shining one, can thee not forgive me my temper and my tongue? Is there nothing in thee which recalls the swift romp of Atlantes' mountain, and thee dancing away from me like a playmate, sharing my joy? *That* is Rogero, good hippogriff, and not the furious mote who offended thee . . . I'll beg thee no more, but pray only that thee might escape thy conscience, as I failed to do when I left my sword and my destiny with Bradamante.

And he comes, he comes, his wings all but folded, backbent, beating a very buzz to fly downward faster than I can fall. And faster he is; he looms to me, blasts himself to one side so close he tumbles me anew, so that the sun is still

above me, but below the mountains turn like clay on a
potter's wheel. The hippogriff's wings are wide now, and
working weightily, and again he grows in mine eye; and now I
can hear him; he is screaming, screaming . . . gods! What a
terror-struck cry! Then the screaming stops, and his lion's
voice rumbles with laughter—ah, he mocks me, he mocks me,
the son of . . . of a mighty gryphon and a blooded mare, most
beautiful of creatures. There, hippogriff: mock me, it is thy
privilege; let me die, it is thy right.

And again the thunder of his humor; he twists his wings,
one up, one down, rolling like a summer swallow; and as I fall
to meet him he is on his back like a swimmer, and, blessed
angel of a hippogriff, he takes me!

I hang from his talons like a newt, mine eyes a-pop from
the pressure of his holding and the surge of his climb; and
climb he must, for he has caught me in a valley, no further
aloft than the height of a tall pine tree; the mountains all
about are above us. He could not have waited the tenth part
of a heartbeat and saved me still. He is confident and
beautiful and he has a most cruel sense of humor.

I am lifted now to his beak; I face his eyes, and from his
open maw his laughter rumbles, and I like a captured puppy
plead to be set down. And indeed, had I a tail I'd wag for
him; I'd whimper if I felt it would reach him.

He dips his head and turns it, and his beak's about my
waist. Now he lifts me, turns his head back to front, lowers
me, twists that my feet may go down and my head up—and I
am astride him again, perched on his shoulders a forearm's
span away from the saddle. He nudges me back, and I bump
my way to the saddle like a babe on a fence-prop, bottom
foremost and clumsy with fright. Not until I am firm in the
saddle does he release me; indeed, for a moment it occurs to
me that, purely in jest, he might bite me in twain once I
think I am safe. Through my thighs I sense another thunder-
ous chuckle at my expense. I bite my lip and cast mine eyes
down, but there is no escaping his mirth.

Now the mountains are behind. The sea is a haze and the sky sea-colored, and where they meet there is no longer a line; by a twist of my mind I may imagine naught but sky around us in an Earthless universe, and a twist again, and it is the sea all about, up and over, my hippogriff and I the sole population of an empty bubble in a universe of water.

And it comes to me then, like a sending—words, odd and small; "Gee," and "Haw," and "Whoa!" and each carries the nostriled flavor of Giles and the smoke in his mouth. So "Gee!" I murmur—and my hippogriff wheels; "Haw," say I, and the other way he turns. . . . I can ride him, fly him! He is mine, he is mine!

But mine too is the humiliation, and the lesson of his laughter, cackling like a conscience. Ahead is the sea, across it adventure and freedom. Behind are the hills, and my sword, my duty, my debt, and a weaponless wench. My steed is silent, as if waiting: "So *haw* then, and let me be damned to my destiny," I cry, and he swings about to tuck the distant shore under his golden chin; to take me back to my grubby fate. And grubby or not, I preen; I am a knight who will not be swayed nor turned aside; straight to my sword I will fly, to mine honor, to—

But below, a clot of white on the rock takes mine eye, and *"Whoa!"* I cry with all my heart; and the hippogriff's bellow of laughter fairly puts whitecaps on the waves below. And down we drop, and down, the roar and crash of beastly laughter in the van, the flanks, the trailing wind of our descent. There is a peal of it for knights without swords, for true courses set and forsaken; there's a rumbling gust of it for gratitude confessed but unpaid, and one for the man who would plan an escape for himself if he were on time to rescue a maiden in peril, or who would plant a bluebell for her if he were late, if he happened to pass that way. But the shrillest laughter, the one having the most cold gold eagle in it, was for a knight who claimed to value his sword for the vows it carried.

I have a moment of shame and one of fury, and then a tortured time of both together. All I need do to cut off this obscene bellowing—ay, and gain the beast's respect, I wouldn't doubt—is to press my heels to his flanks, and straight to Atlantes' mountain we'd go; to Bradamante; to my sword; to the completion of my promises and the payment of my debts.

And it is in the muscles of my legs to draw back those heels; it is in my heart to be humble and accept the beast's deafening censure and cleanse myself; it is, it is, but once again I look below, and am lost; for chained to the rock is a naked woman of such unearthly beauty she can be compared only with the hooded shield I carry . . . with this difference: that whosoever looks upon this shield is blinded, but who looks upon this woman sees so clearly that he cannot live.

Down comes my steed and hovers, searching for a foothold on the windswept rock; and finding it, settles in. Before he is fully earth-borne I am away from him and his subsiding chuckles, slipping and scrambling to the seaward slope. Braced against the iron loops to which she is chained, I cower down close to her, cover mine eyes against that blaze, not of light, but of beauty; and when I can, I peer quickly through my fingers and drink the vision in small and frightened sips.

Her ankles are cruelly bound by a single hoop, hinged, hasped by the double chain which anchored it below. A smaller version of the same device was given each slender wrist, and there she lies, stretched tight against the cold rock, wet with spray, and the wind tugging her hair.

I touch the shackles, the chains. Anchored as they are, it seems the rock itself would lift from the sea bottom before those loops could be drawn. Turning hopelessly from this examination, I meet her eyes and the impact melts me; I fall to my knees and bow my head.

"Who art thou?" she whispers into the shouting wind.

"Rogero, a knight, come to save thee. Who has done this to thee, princess? . . . surely thou art princess . . . ?

"Ay," she breathes, "Angelica of Cathay, shipwrecked here

on the very day the oracle at Ebuda demanded the most beautiful Ebudan maid as a sacrifice to some wrathful god. But since they had me . . . ."

"Ebuda is that village yonder?"

"Ay." Ah, but she is weary; her voice may be heard at all only because its sound was so very different; it differed, almost, from sound itself. "But go not to the village, good knight; they are barbarians and would tear thee to pieces rather than replace me here with one of their own. Best go whence thee came, and my blessing goes with thee; but I am doomed."

"To die of cold and the pecks of sea eagles? I'll die here with thee rather!"

"Nay, it will be quicker than that," she murmurs. "Knowest the monster Orc?" Her eyes are calm, seaward now. As the wind tumbles her hair, I see that it is mystically marked with a stripe of cold silver; there has never been anything so lovely and far away as that swath of starshine.

"Orc? Oh, ay; a legend, a tale to frighten children. He is big as an island and has scales of iron and the tusks of a boar. And thou art chained here for Orc? The eagles will have thee before such a fable comes."

"But he comes now," she says calmly; and two things happen to me which will leave their mark for all my days; one, that as she spoke, grave and quite contained, her tears flowed and I knew that I saw a strength here as wondrous as her beauty; but for the tears, she might have been in her garden, half dreaming and at peace, for all her face showed it. And I turn away from her and see the second thing, the monster Orc.

With a shout I spin to Angelica, take her prisoned hand and on it slip my golden ring. "This will guard thee, Princess!" I cry, and my heart cries with it, *only from my shield,* and I stumble to the hippogriff.

He is ready, flexed, spread, trembling to be off; I have but one foot in the stirrup as he launches himself. The monster comes, and we fly out to meet it; and when we have flown what seemed far enough at first, there is yet another mile to go. It looms over us like a thundercloud; it rises higher and higher from the water, and there is more and still more of it, shapeless, immeasurable, and blind.

Blind! Swordless, lacking pike or halberd, axe or hook, mine only weapon is a giver of blindness; against this, the monster brings the only possible defense; "Blind, it is blind," I cry, and my mount utters a shriek, part despair, but a fine part challenge, and mounts the sky to get above the creature and be sure.

And still it rises until we are but a wasp at a bull's shoulder, until the black rock below is but a steppingstone to this great living hulk.

And the hippogriff, unbidden, folds his wings and we drop, down and down past the upright acres of filthy, streaming iron. I am past thought, incapable of anything except keeping my saddle in the weightless drop. Even my first long fall from the beast's back had seemed not so long as this. Then out come the wings, and I groan against the pressure inside my doublet. Down we go still, the hippogriff battling the wind of our fall, and checking us at last.

We are in a roaring, stinking stream of water and evil fumes, somewhere between Orc's looming bulk and the black rock. Across, and turn, and back, and turn; steamed and spumed and soaked and splattered with stiff salt slime. And for the second time that day I face death despised by the hippogriff . . . .

I see his face again, I think for the last time. And had I years of life to give for the ability to read those bright implacable eyes, I would do it, and gladly; but I've but a few weary minutes. I gaze up hopelessly, and he brings his shining head closer to me, touches my head with a rough gentleness. With his eyes on mine, he makes a single soft sound, and then it is time to turn again. It seems for a moment he cannot and then he does, bravely, and labors back again. Belatedly I see that his wings are wet, and like Pegasus near death in dragon's blood, he cannot remain aloft much longer. Ah, to know what it was he tried to tell me! Who would know? Giles? Ah, but I hate what I was, and what I am . . . .

Together we scream a challenge, and the hippogriff finds strength, somehow, to drive up twice, three times the height of a man and, descending, flutter away a great weight of water from his wings. He passes close to the widening mouth, drives down near the hinge of the jaw just as it emerges. What appears at first as a bony projection from the hinge is suddenly a slimy opal, alight and alive—Orc's eye, set like a whale's. The hippogriff must have known, he must have known!

His small downward drive gives us speed—almost too much. As if alive, however, the shield trembles under my hands, turns to the sun for a bright beam, and hurls it across and back, on, and into the eye. And then we are past and tilting steeply; once more the hippogriff shivers away a mist of heavy water and fights to rise, and back we come the long, long distance around that mountain of a snout, past and past the yawning great arch of the open mouth, to the eye on the other side.

It must be only now that the mighty mass of dim-nerved flesh feels the pain of his dazzle-tattered eye. Something unspeakable moves inside the arch, and a gout of water and ichor shoots skyward. I see it rise, I see it curl; our wings will not survive this, so *"Gee!"* I cry, the sum total of terror and self-hate, of love for the hippogriff and the enchantment of Angelica; of anger, regret, remorse. His response is instant and beyond his control, and he wheels shoreward as I stand on the saddle, fall toward the monster, and kick back at that purple flank with both legs and all my strength. Even as I fall I look back under one arm, for a flash of Angelica's body and the sight of my hippogriff flailing down into the water, short of the shore line. One wet wing-elbow rises like a sail and sinks as slowly; his neck, so pathetically thin without the dry golden ruff of feathers, is stretched toward the rock, but not far enough: he has died for me, and his laughter is dead with him; does thee know now, fool knight, what it was he told thee with that touch of his beak? Only that for all his jibes and hurtful scorn, he was ready to die with thee . . . . And dying, Rogero, thy steed could not know thee heard, or would ever understand.

All this, in the instant of catapult, stretched achingly from my kick, with speed my only wings, my brain racing and my heart wrenched; and before me the magic shield of Atlantes. The shield strikes the water first, and my arrowing body slips under the thundering waterspout as it descends. Like a flat stone the shield skips on its curved face, and my forehead rings it like a gong. It tries to skip again, but my body plops in stingingly at the same instant, and stays it.

And at last I squat in the corner of that beastly smile, and all the hate I have ever known pours out of my arms and into the flailing of the shield. Edge and edge, flat and edge again, I belabor that viscid mound just back of my perch. It yields slowly, and at first I must work with my face but an arrowslength away; I feel it is burning me, filling me with a brutal and primitive madness that surely must turn my brain into what one finds in a dry-rotted chestnut. But then it ceased to be, and was no more, and surely no less horrid than any part of the beast.

How long this pounding? I know not . . . but at length pain reaches it, and a convulsion such as should be impossible to anything so ponderous. My handhold disappears; there is a moment of strangling and a moment of crushing weight, a blow precisely where, earlier, my forehead struck the shield. And then I am thrashing in shallows on black rock, my legs tangled with the limp neck of the hippogriff.

The anchor of the Princess' leg-shackle grinds my small ribs; I shift away from it, clutch it between arm and side, and lock my legs about the neck of the hippogriff, lest his body be swept out to sea. Water runs and runs, tugs and cascades off the rock, and for a long time my sky is full of black specks shifting and twinkling. But I will not let go.

When the tugging stops, I raise my head. The water is back

to something like normal. More than half the hippogriff's body is aground. The rock is completely free of litter—the last cascade having swept it clear. Out at sea stands a new mountain: I think it is dead now. It is sinking, ever so slowly, or sliding down some age-old chute it has worn in the ocean floor.

"Rogero—"

I kick free of the hippogriff's heavy neck and head, and crawl to her.

"Princess!"

"Thou art bravest of knights."

"Nay, Angelica," I mumble. "I am neither brave, nor a knight. I must free thee."

"A simple matter."

"Ay, had I his strength," and I nod to the dead hippogriff.

"Mourn him not, Rogero," says the Princess. "Thee stayed by him as he died, and thee will be rewarded."

"Then must we wait on another hippogriff to strike thy chains?"

"No. The ring, Rogero; take off the ring."

I stumble up the slope to her shackled hand, and take the ring, while she says, "It is a greater amulet, possibly, than thee knows. I was seeking it when I was shipwrecked here; I never thought to see it again; to have it brought to me makes thee part of a miracle."

"See it again? It is thine?"

"It was stolen from my treasure house long ago, and has been on many hands. Its last use, so I was told in the north, was to be by a maiden who wished to free some dolt stupid enough to be entrapped by a magician and too stupid to break free. How came thee by it?"

"It was . . . cast aside as worthless." My ears burn. "Princess, I must free thee."

In her chains, she stretches lazily. "Whenever we like. These bonds mean nothing. Rogero, I am in thy debt."

"No, Princess, for I have seen thee. It is enough."

"Prettily said, and I believe thee." And it seems she is amused. "Then do as I ask, and thee shall see a new power of the ring. Put the ring in my mouth."

I held it to her parted lips. "Thou art a sweet and somewhat slow-witted man," she whispers. "Goodbye, Rogero." She takes the ring.

The shackles lie empty, and I crouch there over the black rock which pillowed her, my one hand extended, my mind awhirl at the nearness . . . .

Nearness? She is gone!

Ah, she might have told me of this magic before demonstrating it! Is the world and all its magics leagued against me? Has the universe itself been designed to make me out a fool? "Thou art a sweet and somewhat slow-witted man." *Aiee!* I shall have that carven on my tomb!

Slowly I mount the rock, and face the rocky spine leading to the mainland, to and through the barbarians; through mountains and hunger and poverty and illness; to aid and be aided along the way, until at last I have won what was given me and what, unearned, was cast aside; afoot, acrawl—to my destiny.

"Are you quite all right, sir?"

Now that, old Dean-head, is a question. The music is surf and feathers in all its upbeats, strictly society on the down: scherzophrenic. A hot, transparent, blue flame whuffs out, and suddenly that is a matter of supreme importance, though I can't think why. Slowly I look up at him. "Me?"

"It seemed for a second or two that you weren't quite—with us, sir."

"A second or two," I say, "that's all it takes." Now I remember: that blue flame on the jubilee tray is the one I was looking at when I went under, or other, or wherever Rogero keeps his world. Surely I know where that is! I look up again. Deans read books. "Listen, what do you know about Atlantes?"

62

"Atlantis, sir?" This guy, you couldn't ruffle him with a williwaw. "As I recall, it sank under the sea."

"No, Atlant*es*—a magician."

"Ah. I believe there was a necromancer of that name in Ariosto, somewhere."

I put an accurate forefinger on his second stud and push it triumphantly. "*Orlando Furioso!* So *that's* it! Hey, do you remember what ever happened to Bradamante?"

He puts his hands behind his back and looks at the wall meeting the ceiling. Good head on that man; splendid. "As I remember, sir, she married a knight—"

"*Ex*-knight," I say, and it hurts. "Also, good night." I give him a whole heap of money and head out.

"Good night, sir," says the doorman.

"Oh," I say, "you. Hey, a girl about so high and so wide with a silver streak in her hair, she left here. How long ago?"

He says he doesn't recall so I give him some money. "About four minutes," he says. "That way," and points.

"Only four?" I have something in me like a pain. "That way, you're sure?"

"You should be able to catch her," he says. He closes his eyes and smiles. "Pretty."

"The Grand Canyon," I say, "it's cute too." I run the way he points. It's to the river.

So it's *Orlando* all this time, I think, and something has kept me from recognizing it. Atlantes and Bradamante, Angelica, princess of Cathay, the hippogriff and the Orc, all there. And what am I doing, acting it out? Atlantes kept Rogero from being a knight; some sort of magic keeps me from being a painter. Only nowadays they call it a neurosis.

So where am I going in such a hurry?

Got to save the Princess from the Orc. Orc, variant of urp, a real nauseating beast. Better I should go right back to the studio and mind my own business. Yes, that's what Rogero kept telling himself. And he landed by the Princess anyway, no matter how his hippogriff laughed. Well laugh then, hippogriff. You're not long for this world anyway. There she is!

Walk now. Get your wind. See what happens to her. She's chained naked on no rock yet. Or maybe she is . . . analogies being what they are . . . .

Now cut it out, Giles! You're all right now. It's all just a story you read and mooned over when you were a kid. There were others; but did you really live it up with "The Little Lame Prince"; did you referee that go between the firedrake and the remora in Andrew Lang's book; did you feel the icicle pierce your heart in "Back of the North Wind"? So maybe your subconscious is trying to tell you something with Ariosto. Tell you what? To get religion? Or (and this is the idea that feels like pain) that you're no more a painter than Rogero is a knight, in the long run . . . in spite of some initial successes?

Go home, go home, and paint the way Miss Brandt wants you to. Go home now and your hippogriff will love you for it; yes, and live, whatever that might mean.

But wait; Miss Brandt wants you to be a painter and Bradamante didn't want Rogero to be a knight. My story doesn't coincide with his; it just sort of resonates. All the more reason to get out of here, Giles; go home. You've got all the money in the world; all the freedom, all the time to go anywhere and do anything. *Paint anything.* You know what happened to Rogero, his hippogriff, and his magic ring—yes, and his shield too, when he let his bumbling chivalry override his derisive conscience. (Conscience? Since when can a conscience be as beautiful as a hippogriff?)

So, go home. But look; look there, she has stopped at the River Road, and stands under a light, her gray silk gone all silver and the margins of her hair sinking a little over her slender shoulders as she raises her face to the sky. What is in that face? I can't see, I can't see . . . an appeal, a submission rather; such sadness as hers is past hope and therefore past appealing to anything.

Princess, what is your rock, what your Orc? What comes, and you helpless; what shows itself without form, grows to fill the sky; what is impregnable, ironclad, and filthy, unspeakable? What fills your world and your short future, and proves at the same time that it shows only its slimy skull, and there is measurelessly more below?

You don't scream, Princess?

You are only calm; but I have seen your tears.

She crosses the road to the trees, and takes a path toward the water; so laugh, hippogriff. I'll go to her.

But she's gone in the shadows: hurry, hurry—

And there in a quiet place I come on her and, like Rogero on the black rock, I sip the vision; for to gulp it would be more than I could bear.

There is a hole in the grove, an empty place by the water to let the night in. Part of a moon floats a train across the water to her as she sinks to a bench. Her head turns and tilts a little, as if to a footfall (does she hear me? Does she know there is more than her sadness in the world?) and she is completely in silhouette except for the single beam cupping a cheekbone, and the silver streak in her hair; with that small shard of cold white, the path on the water has a part of moon at each end!

And still more, just a little, her head turns, so her perfect profile lies in liquid moon; and now, if she turns only her eyes, she may see me. She does.

"I knew you'd be around." Her voice . . . a bell, a bird, a sound-unlike-sound . . . no. A voice, just a voice. Think about that, Giles; but not now.

"May I . . . I mean . . . ."

"Sure," she says, indicating the bench. "Why not?"

I sit timidly at the other end of the bench, watching her as she stares out over the water. Her eyes are hooded and her face a chalice of sadness, brimming. And suddenly I know her Orc.

Poverty can be the Orc. Poverty can be the monster visible and nearing, which comes slimy and stinking out of the pit to fill the sky and yet be showing only its smallest part. Poverty can come to one chained, disregard one's station and one's virtues, and take one at its leisure.

Then I might be Rogero yet, for there is money in my pocket, neat, obedient, omnipotent money. Should I challenge her monster?

She might be angry. (Angelica? Angry? No; she bade the knight leave her and save himself.)

I look at her, and the sadness in her is greater than the money in my pocket. I see abruptly that my gesture would not anger her after all. She would simply pity me. My effort would be lost in her great need.

Then I'll share what I have. Half what I have is still, effectively, all the money there is.

She is looking at the moon, so distant and so dead; she has the mark of distance and death upon her. Rogero offered no part of himself to his princess; he offered it all.

All of it? I touch the lapel of the most expensive suit I have ever owned; good new money whispers under my hand of miles and years of color and startlement, tastes and textures and toys; all the things, the thrills I've never had because it took too much time to be just Giles.

"I wish you wouldn't stare like that."

"I'm sorry," I whisper. "Sorry."

"What's on your mind?"

Only that when tomorrow's sun comes to you, you might give back to it as much gladness as a daffodil. Just that by giving you all I ever owned, so new that my own hands have not touched it, you might never be afraid again. "Just that I'd like to . . . borrow your pen."

"My—well, I suppose." She has it in her handbag; finds it and gives it to me.

I take my elegant, one-and-final blue book, and crouching close in the moonlight, *Giles,* I write, *Giles,* and *Giles,* and *Giles,* until I've written on the bottom line of every perforated page.

I hold it out to her with the pen. Here (I would say, but I

cannot speak) here is all the magic I own, since I lost my shield. Here are my hooves and my talons. Here are my wings.

"What's this?"

"Yours," I croak. "I don't want it. Any of it."

"God," she says.

She rises like the lily—but now, in the moonlight, more like a cereus—and looks at me. "You're sure, now."

"Never more sure."

"I thought," she says, "that you'd turn out to be a lot more fun than this." And she throws the book into the river.

I sit in a dream by the corpse of a dream. It grows cold. Loneliness lives in my very pores as sadness lives in her face. She is gone, the moon is gone, and something else has gone, too. I do not know its name but it once kept me warm.

When she left, her leaving a completion of the absent gesture of throwing the book, I said nothing and I did not move; I am not sure that I really saw her leave.

Rogero, I think, I need you. I wish I could have a word with you.

For when you were stripped and alone, somewhere in yourself you found a way to travel, through wild countries, through poverty and sickness and hardship, certain that they would refine you for your destiny. You see, dear dopple, the twentieth-century man has no destiny; at least, he has no magicians to read it off for him, so he can never quite be sure. But take his amulets away, his spells and cantrips graven with the faces of dead presidents—and he'll look over no mountains toward an unshakable faith. He'll stare at nothing but his own terror.

Rogero, the universe is indeed leagued together to make fools of us.

I leave the bench and the river, not to be a pilgrim, but just to take my misery to familiar surroundings and wrap it up in weariness. And tomorrow I shall wake with the comfort—if such it is—that I am Giles and will continue to be Giles without the intrusion of Signor Ariosto's parables. It had better be a comfort; I may not even turn my staring white canvas to the wall, now that I think of it; I wouldn't be able to bring myself to touch it.

So I walk and I walk. And then up the long steps and down the long hall, fling open the door which unveils the dirty—

But it isn't a dirty bed, and I have one mad moment of childish panic; I have burst into the wrong place; and then I see the easel, the bright clean easel, and I know I am home.

"I hope you don't mind; the door was open, and I thought . . . so to keep myself busy while I waited, I—" She makes a smile, and tries harder and makes another, but smiles over hands which rapidly clasp and unclasp are unconvincing. "I'll go," says Miss Brandt, "but I wanted to tell you I think you did a splendid thing."

I look at the clean, shelved dishes and the drum-tight bedclothes, and my paints and brushes sensibly left untouched. But what impresses me is the unthinkable statement that I have done a splendid thing. I sit on the bed and look at her.

"How did you ever find out?" she asks. "You weren't to know, ever."

"I know a lot now," I tell her. "What specially do you mean?"

"About the money. Giving it back."

"I gave it away," I admit. And, because it's the truth. "I don't call that so splendid."

"It was, if . . . ." And then, as if she's had the question held down tight and can't control it any longer, she flashes a glance at the easel, and asks, "Does it mean you'll paint again?"

My eye follows hers and I shudder. She turns pale as the new light at the window. "Oh," she says in a very small voice. "I—guess I've done the wrong thing." She snatches up a shiny black pocketbook and runs to the door. But there's a Giles standing there first, who pushes her back hard so she sits down—*plump!*—on the bed.

I am tired and hurt and disappointed and I want no more

wonderments. "You tell me all the things you've done, wrong and otherwise, right from the beginning."

"Oh, how it began. Well, I'm her secretary, you know, and we had a sort of quarrel about you. She's a mean, small, stupid sort of person, Giles, for all her money and the way she looks—she is lovely, isn't she? In case you want to know (everybody does) that streak of silver is real. Anyway, I—"

"You're *her* secretary?"

"Yes. Well I got so terribly distressed about"—she waves at the easel again, and the miraculous lashes point away—"you, you know, that I suppose I got on her nerves. She said some mean things about you and I sort of blew up. I said if I had her money I'd see to it that you started painting again."

"Just like that."

"I'm sorry. It was—so important; I couldn't bear to have you just—"

"Go on with the story."

"She said if I had her money and tried to use it that way I'd just make a fool of myself. Well, maybe she was right, but . . . it went like that until she swore at me and said if I was so positive, go ahead. Take all the money I wanted and just see how far I'd get." All the while she talks she is pleading, underneath. I don't listen to that part of it. "So I came here yesterday and I was to phone her the way you sign your name, and she would call the bank and fix it up."

"Nice of her."

"No it wasn't. She did it because she thought it would be amusing. She has so much money that it wouldn't cost her anything. Anything she'd notice. And then you found out about it, I don't know how, and gave her the checkbook. When she came back last night she was wild. It wasn't half the fun she thought. All you did was to be amusing in a restaurant for a couple of hours. Please don't look at me like that. I just did what I could. I—had to. Please—I had to."

I keep on looking at her, thinking. Finally, "Miss Brandt, you said a thing yesterday—my God, was it only yesterday?—about my not being able to paint now because I don't know why I painted before. Do you know what you were talking about?"

"I—" and the lashes go down, the hands busy themselves, "—I only know sort of generally. I mean, if you can do a thing and know how you do it and—and especially *why,* and then something stops you, I think it's easy to see the thing that stops you."

So I lean against the door and look at her in the way that makes her squirm (I'm sorry but that's the way I look when I'm thinking) and I think:

Does anyone ask a painter—even the painter himself—*why* he paints? Now me, I painted . . . used to . . . whatever I saw that was beautiful. It had to be beautiful to me, through and through, before I would paint it. And I used to be a pretty simple fellow, and found many completely beautiful things to paint.

But the older you get the fewer completely beautiful things you see. Every flower has a brown spot somewhere, and a hippogriff has evil laughter. So at some point in his development an artist has to paint, not what he sees (which is what I've always done) but the beauty in what he sees. Most painters, I think, cross this line early; I'm crossing it late.

And the simple—child?—artist paints for himself . . . but when he grows up he sees through the eyes of the beholder, and feels through his fingertips, and helps him to see that which the artist is gifted to see. Those who had wept over my work up to now, I used to say, had stolen meanings out of it, against my will. When I grow up, perhaps they will accept what I willingly give them. And because Miss Brandt feels this is worth giving, she has tried to get more of it for people.

So I had stopped painting because I had become too discerning, and could find nothing perfect enough to paint. But now it occurs to me that the girl with the silver in her hair can be painted for the beauty she has, regardless of her other ugliness. Atlantes had a magic, and in it one walked the battlements of a bastion—which was only, in truth, a byre. Miss Brandt can paint me, in her mind, as a man who turned back all the money in the world, and, for her, this is a real nobility.

The only key to the complexity of living is to understand that this world contains two-and-a-half-billion worlds, each built in a person's eyes and all different, and all susceptible to beauty and hungry for it.

I ran out of things to paint . . . and now, now, there'll never be enough time to paint beauty! Rogero did a knightly thing on the black rock, because he was not a good knight. I did a manly thing about the money because I was a fool. All successes are accidents in someone's world . . . so: "You tell her it worked, Miss Brandt. I'm going to paint, Miss Brandt; I'm going to paint *you,* Miss Brandt, because you're beautiful."

And I paint, and she is, because I paint, because she is.

Slow Sculpture

She didn't know who he was when she met him; well, not many people did. He was in the high orchard doing something under a pear tree. The land smelled of late summer and wind: bronze, it smelled bronze. He looked up at a compact girl in her mid-twenties, with a fearless face and eyes the same color as her hair, which was extraordinary because her hair was red-gold. She looked down at a leather-skinned man in his forties with a gold-leaf electroscope in his hand, and felt she was an intruder. She said, "Oh," in what was apparently the right way, because he nodded once and said, "Hold this," and there could then be no thought of intrusion. She knelt down by him and took the instrument, holding it just where he positioned her hand, and then he moved a little away and struck a tuning-fork against his kneecap. "What's it doing?" He had a good voice, the kind of voice strangers notice and listen to.

She looked at the delicate leaves of gold in the glass shield of the electroscope. "They're moving apart."

He struck the tuning fork again and the leaves pressed away from one another. "Much?"

"About forty-five degrees when you hit the fork."

"Good—that's about the most we'll get." From a pocket of his bush jacket he drew a sack of chalk-dust and dropped a small handful on the ground. "I'll move now. You stay right there and tell me how much the leaves separate."

He traveled around the pear tree in a zigzag course, striking his tuning fork while she called out numbers—ten degrees, thirty, five, twenty, nothing. Whenever the gold foil pressed apart to maximum, forty degrees or more, he dropped more chalk. When he was finished the tree was surrounded, in a rough oval, by the white dots of chalk. He took out a notebook and diagrammed them and the tree, and put away the book, and took the electroscope out of her hands. "Were you looking for something?" he asked her.

"No," she said. "Yes."

He could smile. Though it did not last long, she found it very surprising in a face like that. "That's not what is called, in a court of law, a responsive answer."

She glanced across the hillside, metallic in that late light. There wasn't much on it—rocks, weeds the summer was done with, a tree or so, and then the orchard. Anyone present had come a long way to get here. "It wasn't a simple question," she said, tried to smile, and burst into tears.

She was sorry and said so.

"Why?" he asked. This was the first time she was to experience this ask-the-next-question thing of his. It was unsettling. It always would be—never less, sometimes a great deal more. "Well—one doesn't have emotional explosions in public."

"*You* do. I don't know this 'one' you're talking about."

"I—guess I don't either, now that you mention it."

"Tell the truth then. No sense in going round and round about it, 'he'll think that I—' and the like. I'll think what I think, whatever you say. Or—go on down the mountain and just don't say any more." She did not turn to go, so he added, "Try the truth, then. If it's important, it's simple, and if it's simple it's easy to say."

"I'm going to die!" she cried.

"So am I."

"I have a lump in my breast."

73

"Come up to the house and I'll fix it."

Without another word he turned away and started through the orchard. Startled half out of her wits, indignant and full of insane hope, experiencing, even, a quick curl of astonished laughter, she stood for a moment watching him go, and then found herself (at what point did I decide?) running after him.

She caught up with him on the uphill margin of the orchard. "Are you a doctor?"

He appeared not to notice that she had waited, had run. "No," he said, and, walking on, appeared not to see her stand again pulling at her lower lip, then run again to catch up.

"I must be out of my mind," she said, joining him on a garden path. She said it to herself, which he must have known because he did not answer. The garden was alive with defiant chrysanthemums and a pond in which she saw the flicker of a pair of redcap imperials—silver, not gold fish—which were the largest she had ever seen. Then—the house.

First it was part of the garden, with its colonnaded terrace, and then, with its rock walls (too big to be called fieldstone) part of the mountain. It was on and in the hillside, and its roofs paralleled the skylines, front and sides, and part of it was backed against an outjutting cliff face. The door, beamed and studded and with two archers' slits, was opened for them (but there was no one there) and when it closed it was silent, a far more solid exclusion of things outside than any click or clang of latch or bolt. She stood with her back against it watching him cross what seemed to be the central well of the house, or at least this part of it. It was a kind of small court in the center of which was an atrium, glazed on all of its five sides and open to the sky at the top. In it was a tree, a cypress or juniper, gnarled and twisted and with the turned-back, paralleled, sculptured appearance of what the Japanese call bonsai.

"Aren't you coming?" he called, holding open a door behind the atrium.

"Bonsai just aren't fifteen feet tall," she said.

"This one is."

She came by it slowly, looking. "How long have you had it?"

His tone of voice said he was immensely pleased. It is a clumsiness to ask the owner of a bonsai how old it is; you are then demanding to know if it is his work or if he has acquired and continued the concept of another; you are tempting him to claim for his own the concept and the meticulous labor of someone else, and it becomes rude to tell a man he is being tested. Hence "How long have you had it?" is polite, forbearing, profoundly courteous. He answered, "Half my life." She looked at the tree. Trees can be found, sometimes, not quite discarded, not quite forgotten, potted in rusty gallon cans in not quite successful nurseries, unsold because they are shaped oddly or have dead branches here and there, or because they have grown too slowly in whole or part. These are the ones which develop interesting trunks and a resistance to misfortune that makes them flourish if given the least excuse for living. This one was far older than half this man's life, or all of it. Looking at it, she was terrified by the unbidden thought that a fire, a family of squirrels, some subterranean worm or termite could end this beauty—something working outside any concept of rightness or justice or . . . or respect. She looked at the tree. She looked at the man.

"Coming?"

"Yes," she said and went with him into his laboratory. "Sit down over there and relax," he told her. "This might take a little while."

"Over there" was a big leather chair by the bookcase. The books were right across the spectrum—reference works in medicine and engineering, nuclear physics, chemistry, biology, psychiatry. Also tennis, gymnastics, chess, the oriental war game Go, and golf. And then drama, the techniques of fiction, *Modern English Usage, The American Language* and supplement, Wood's and Walker's rhyming dictionaries and an array of other dictionaires and encyclopedias. A whole long shelf of biographies. "You have quite a library."

He answered her rather shortly: clearly he did not want to
talk just now, for he was very busy. He said only, "Yes I
have—perhaps you'll see it some time," which left her to pick
away at his words to find out what on earth he meant by
them. He could only have meant, she decided, that the books
beside her chair were what he kept handy for his work—that
his real library was elsewhere. She looked at him with a
certain awe.

And she watched him. She liked the way he moved—swiftly, decisively. Clearly he knew what he was doing. He used
some equipment that she recognized—a glass still, titration
equipment, a centrifuge. There were two refrigerators, one of
which was not a refrigerator at all, for she could see the large
indicator on the door: it stood at 70°F. It came to her that
a modern refrigerator is perfectly adaptable to the demand
for controlled environment, even a warm one.

But all that, and the equipment she did not recognize, was
only furniture. It was the man who was worth watching, the
man who kept her occupied so that not once in all the long
time she sat there was she tempted toward the bookshelves.

At last he finished a long sequence at the bench, threw
some switches, picked up a tall stool and came over to her.
He perched on the stool, hung his heels on the cross-spoke,
and lay a pair of long brown hands over his knees. "Scared?"

"I s'pose I am."

"You don't have to stay."

"Considering the alternative," she began bravely, but the
courage-sound somehow oozed out, "it can't matter much."

"Very sound," he said, almost cheerfully. "I remember
when I was a kid there was a fire scare in the apartment
house where we lived. It was a wild scramble to get out, and
my ten-year-old brother found himself outside in the street
with an alarm clock in his hand. It was an old one and it
didn't work—but of all the things in the place he might have
snatched up at a time like that, it turned out to be the clock.
He's never been able to figure out why."

"Have you?"

"Not why he picked that particular thing, no. But I think I know why he did something obviously irrational. You see, panic is a very special state. Like fear and flight, or fury and attack, it's a pretty primitive reaction to extreme danger. It's one of the expressions of the will to survive. What makes it so special is that it's irrational. Now, why would the abandonment of reason be a survival mechanism?"

She thought about this seriously. There was that about this man which made serious thought imperative. "I can't imagine," she said finally. "Unless it's because, in some situations, reason just doesn't work."

"You *can* imagine," he said, again radiating that huge approval, making her glow. "And you just did. If you are in danger and you try reason, and reason doesn't work, you abandon it. You can't say it's unintelligent to abandon what doesn't work, right? So then you are in panic; then you start to perform random acts. Most of them—far and away most—will be useless; some might even be dangerous, but that doesn't matter—you're in danger already. Where the survival factor comes in is that away down deep you know that one chance in a million is better than no chance at all. So—here you sit—you're scared and you could run; something says you should run; but you won't."

She nodded.

He went on: "You found a lump. You went to a doctor and he made some tests and gave you the bad news. Maybe you went to another doctor and he confirmed it. You then did some research and found out what was to happen next—the exploratory, the radical, the questionable recovery, the whole long agonizing procedure of being what they call a terminal case. You then flipped out. Did some things you hope I won't ask you about. Took a trip somewhere, anywhere, wound up in my orchard for no reason." He spread the good hands and let them go back to their kind of sleep. "Panic. The reason for little boys in their pajamas standing at midnight with a broken alarm clock in their arms, and for the existence of quacks." Something chimed over on the bench and he gave her a quick smile and went back to work, saying over his shoulder: "I'm not a quack, by the way. To qualify as a quack you have to claim to be a doctor. I don't."

She watched him switch off, switch on, stir, measure and calculate. A little orchestra of equipment chorused and soloed around him as he conducted, whirring, hissing, clicking, flickering. She wanted to laugh, to cry, and to scream. She did no one of these things for fear of not stopping, ever.

When he came over again, the conflict was not raging within her, but exerting steady and opposed tensions; the result was a terrible stasis, and all she could do when she saw the instrument in his hand was to widen her eyes. She quite forgot to breathe.

"Yes, it's a needle," he said, his tone almost bantering. "A long shiny sharp needle. Don't tell me you are one of those needle-shy people." He flipped the long power-cord which trailed from the black housing around the hypodermic, to get some slack, and straddled the stool. "Want something to steady your nerves?"

She was afraid to speak; the membrane containing her sane self was very thin, stretched very tight.

He said, "I'd rather you didn't, because this pharmaceutical stew is complex enough as it is. But if you need it. . . ."

She managed to shake her head a little, and again she felt the wave of approval from him. There were a thousand questions she wanted to ask—had meant to ask—needed to ask: What was in the needle? How many treatments must she have? What would they be like? How long must she stay, and where? And most of all—oh, could she live, could she live?

He seemed concerned with the answer to only one of these. "It's mostly built around an isotope of potassium. If I told you all I know about it and how I came on it in the first place, it would take—well, more time than we've got. But here's the general idea: Theoretically, every atom is electrically balanced (never mind ordinary exceptions). Likewise all electrical charges in the molecule are supposed to be balanced—so much plus, so much minus, total zero. I happened on the fact that the balance of charges in a wild cell is not zero—not quite. It's as if there was a submicroscopic thunderstorm going on at the molecular level, with little lightning bolts flashing back and forth and changing the signs. Interfering with communications—static—and that," he said, gesturing with the shielded hypo in his hand, "is what this is all about. When something interferes with communications— especially the RNA mechanism, which says, Read this blueprint and build accordingly, and stop when it's done—when that message gets garbled, lopsided things get built, off-balance things, things which do almost what they should, do it almost right: they're wild cells, and the messages they pass on are even worse.

"Okay: Whether these thunderstorms are caused by viruses or chemicals or radiation or physical trauma or even anxiety—and don't think anxiety can't do it—that's secondary. The important thing is to fix it so the thunderstorm can't happen. If you can do that, the cells have plenty of ability all by themselves to repair and replace what's gone wrong. And biological systems aren't like ping-pong balls with static charges waiting for the charge to leak away or to discharge into a grounded wire. They have a kind of resilience—I call it forgiveness—which enables them to take on a little more charge, or a little less, and do all right. Well then: Say a certain clump of cells is wild and say it carries an aggregate of a hundred units extra on the positive side. Cells immediately around it are affected, but not the next layer or the next.

"If they could be opened to the extra charge, if they could help to drain it off, they would, well, *cure* the wild cells of the surplus, you see what I mean? And they would be able to handle that little overage themselves, or pass it on to other cells and still others who could deal with it. In other words, if I can flood your body with some medium which can drain off and distribute a concentration of this unbalanced charge, the ordinary bodily processes will be free to move in and clear up the wild-cell damage. And that's what I have here."

He held the shielded needle between his knees and from a

79

side pocket of his lab coat he took a plastic box, opened it and drew out an alcohol swab. Still cheerfully talking, he took her terror-numbed arm and scrubbed at the inside of her elbow. "I am not for one second implying that nuclear charges in the atom are the same thing as static electricity. They're in a different league altogether. But the analogy holds. I could use another analogy. I could liken the charge on the wild cells to accumulations of fat, and this gunk of mine to a detergent, which would break it up and spread it so far it couldn't be detected any more. But I'm led to the static analogy by an odd side effect—organisms injected with this stuff do build up one hell of a static charge. It's a by-product, and for reasons I can only theorize about at the moment, it seems to be keyed to the audio spectrum. Tuning forks and the like. That's what I was playing with when I met you. That tree is drenched with this stuff. It used to have a whorl of wild-cell growth. It hasn't any more." He gave her the quick surprising smile and let it click away as he held the needle point upward and squirted it. With his other hand wrapped around her left biceps, he squeezed gently and firmly. The needle was lowered and placed and slid into the big vein so deftly that she gasped—not because it hurt, but because it did not. Attentively he watched the bit of glass barrel protruding from a black housing as he withdrew the plunger a fraction and saw the puff of red into the colorless fluid inside, and then he bore steadily on the plunger again.

"Please don't move. . . . I'm sorry; this will take a little time. I have to get quite a lot of this into you. Which is fine, you know," he said, resuming the tone of his previous remarks about audio spectra, "because side effect or no, it's consistent. Healthy bio systems develop a strong electrostatic field, unhealthy ones a weak one or none at all. With an instrument as primitive and simple as that little electroscope you can tell if any part of the organism has a community of wild cells, and if so, where it is and how big and how wild." Deftly he shifted his grip on the encased hypodermic without moving the point or varying the amount of plunger pressure.

It was beginning to be uncomfortable, an ache turning into a bruise. "And if you're wondering why this mosquito has a housing on it with a wire attached (although I'll bet you're not and that you know as well as I do that I'm doing all this talking just to keep your mind occupied!) I'll tell you. It's nothing but a coil carrying a high-frequency alternating current. The alternating field sees to it that the fluid is magnetically and electrostatically neutral right from the start." He withdrew the needle suddenly and smoothly, bent her arm, and trapped in the inside of her elbow a cotton swab.

"Nobody ever told me that before after a treatment," she said.

"What?"

"No charge," she said.

Again that wave of approval, this time with words: "I like your style. How do you feel?"

She cast about for accurate phrases. "Like the owner of a large sleeping hysteria begging someone not to wake it up."

He laughed. "In a little while you are going to feel so weird you won't have time for hysteria." He got up and returned the needle to the bench, looping up the cable as he went. He turned off the AC field and returned with a large glass bowl and a square of plywood. He inverted the bowl on the floor near her and placed the wood on its broad base.

"I remember something like that," she said. "When I was in—in junior high school. They were generating artificial lightning with a . . . let me see . . . well, it had a long endless belt running over pulleys and some little wires scraping on it and a big copper ball on top."

"Van de Graaf generator."

"Right! And they did all sorts of things with it, but what I specially remember is standing on a piece of wood on a bowl like that and they charged me up with the generator, and I didn't feel much of anything except all my hair stood out from my head. Everyone laughed. I looked like a golliwog. They said I was carrying forty thousand volts."

"Good! I'm glad you remember that. This'll be a little different, though. By roughly another forty thousand."

"Oh!"

"Don't worry. Long as you're insulated, and as long as grounded, or comparatively grounded objects—me, for example—stay well away from you, there won't be any fireworks."

"Are you going to use a generator like that?"

"Not like that, and I already did. You're the generator."

"I'm—*oh!*" She had raised her hand from the upholstered chair arm and there was a crackle of sparks and the faint smell of ozone.

"Oh you sure are, and more than I thought, and quicker. Get up!"

She started up slowly; she finished the maneuver with speed. As her body separated from the chair she was, for a fractional second, seated in a tangle of spitting blue-white threads. They, or she, propelled her a yard and a half away, standing. Literally shocked half out of her wits, she almost fell.

"Stay on your feet!" he snapped, and she recovered, gasping. He stepped back a pace. "Get up on the board. Quick, now!"

She did as she was told, leaving, for the two paces she traveled, two brief footprints of fire. She teetered on the board. Visibly, her hair began to stir. "What's happening to me?" she cried.

"You're getting charged after all," he said jovially, but at this point she failed to appreciate the extension of even her own witticism. She cried again, "What's happening to me?"

"It's all right," he said consolingly. He went to the bench and turned on a tone generator. It moaned deep in the one to three hundred cycle range. He increased the volume and turned the pitch control. It howled upward and as it did so her red-gold hair shivered and swept up and out, each hair attempting frantically to get away from all the others. He ran the tone up above ten thousand cycles and all the way back to a belly-bumping inaudible eleven; at the extremes her hair slumped, but at around eleven hundred it stood out in (as she had described it) golliwog style.

He turned down the gain to a more or less bearable level and picked up the electroscope. He came toward her, smiling. "You *are* an electroscope, you know that? And a living Van de Graaf generator as well. And a golliwog."

"Let me down," was all she could say.

"Not yet. Please hang tight. The differential between you and everything else here is so high that if you got near any of it you'd discharge into it. It wouldn't harm you—it isn't current electricity—but you might get a burn and a nervous shock out of it." He held out the electroscope; even at that distance, and in her distress, she could see the gold leaves writhe apart. He circled her, watching the leaves attentively, moving the instrument forward and back and from side to side. Once he went to the tone generator and turned it down some more. "You're sending such a strong field I can't pick up the variations," he explained, and returned to her, closer now.

"I can't, much more . . . I can't," she murmured; he did not hear, or he did not care. He moved the electroscope near her abdomen, up and from side to side.

"Yup. There you are!" he said cheerfully, moving the instrument close to her right breast.

"What?" she whimpered.

"Your cancer. Right breast, low, around toward the arm-pit." He whistled. "A mean one, too. Malignant as hell."

She swayed and then collapsed forward and down. A sick blackness swept down on her, receded explosively in a glare of agonizing blue-white, and then crashed down on her like a mountain falling.

Place where wall meets ceiling. Another wall, another ceiling. Hadn't seen it before. Didn't matter. Don't care.
Sleep.

Place where wall meets ceiling. Something in the way. His

face, close, drawn, tired; eyes awake though and penetrating. Doesn't matter. Don't care.

Sleep.

Place where wall meets ceiling. Down a bit, late sunlight. Over a little, rusty-gold chrysanthemums in a goldgreen glass cornucopia. Something in the way again: his face.

"Can you hear me?"

Yes, but don't answer. Don't move. Don't speak.

Sleep.

It's a room, a wall, a table, a man pacing; a nighttime window and mums you'd think were alive, but don't you know they're cut right off and dying?

Do they know that?

"How are you?" Urgent, urgent.

"Thirsty."

Cold and a bite to it that aches the hinges of the jaws. Grapefruit juice. Lying back on his arm while he holds the glass in the other hand, oh no, that's not . . . "Thank you. Thanks very—" Try to sit up, the sheet—*my clothes!*

"Sorry about that," he said, the mindreader-almost. "Some things that have to be done just aren't consistent with panty-hose and a mini-dress. All washed and dried and ready for you, though—any time. Over there."

The brown wool and the panty-hose and the shoes, on the chair. He's respectful, standing back, putting the glass next to an insulated carafe on the night-table.

"What things?"

"Throwing up. Bedpans," he said candidly.

Protective with the sheet, which can hide bodies but oh not embarrassment. "Oh I'm sorry. . . . Oh. I must've—" Shake head and he slides back and forth in the vision.

"You went into shock, and then you just didn't come out of it." He hesitated. It was the first time she had ever seen him hesitate over anything. She became for a moment an almost-mind-reader: *Should I tell her what's in my mind?*

Sure he should, and he did: "You didn't *want* to come out of it."

"It's all gone out of my head."

"The pear tree, the electroscope. The injection, the electro-static response."

"No," she said, not knowing, then, knowing: *"No!"*

"Hang on!" he rapped, and next thing she knew he was by the bed, over her, his two hands hard on her cheeks. "Don't slip off again. You can handle it. You can handle it because it's all right now, do you understand that? You're all right!"

"You told me I had cancer." It sounded pouty, accusing. He laughed at her, actually laughed.

"You told *me* you had it."

"Oh, but I didn't *know.*"

"That explains it, then," he said in a load-off-my-back tone. "There wasn't anything in what I did that could cause a three-day withdrawal like that; it had to be something in you."

"Three *days!*"

He simply nodded in response to that and went on with what he was saying. "I get a little pompous once in a while," he said engagingly. "Comes from being right so much of the time. Took a bit more for granted than I should have, didn't I? when I assumed you'd been to a doctor, maybe even had a biopsy. You didn't, did you?"

"I was afraid," she admitted. She looked at him. "My mother died of it, and my aunt, and my sister had a radical mastectomy. I couldn't bear it. And when you—"

"When I told you what you already knew, and what you never wanted to hear, you couldn't take it. You blacked right out, you know. Fainted away, and it had nothing to do with the seventy-odd thousand volts of static you were carrying. I caught you." He put out his arms and instinctively she shrank back, but he held the arms where they were, on display, until she looked at them and saw the angry red scorch marks on his forearms and the heavy biceps, as much of them as she could see from under his short-sleeved shirt. "About nine-

85

tenths knocked me out too," he said, "but at least you didn't crack your head or anything."

"Thank you," she said reflexively, and then began to cry. "What am I going to *do?*"

"Do? Go back home, wherever that is—pick up your life again, whatever that might mean."

"But you said—"

"When are you going to get it into your head that what I did was not a diagnostic?"

"Are you—did you—you mean you cured it?"

"I mean you're curing it right now. I explained it all to you before—you remember that now, don't you?"

"Not altogether, but—yes." Surreptitiously (but not enough, because he saw her) she felt under the sheet for the lump. "It's still there."

"If I bopped you over the head with a bat," he said with slightly exaggerated simplicity, "there would be a lump on it. It would be there tomorrow and the next day. The day after that it might be smaller, and in a week you'd still be able to feel it, but it would be gone. Same thing here."

At last she let the enormity of it touch her. "A one-shot cure for cancer. . . ."

"Oh God," he said harshly, "I can tell by looking at you that I am going to have to listen to that speech *again*. Well, I won't."

Startled, she said, "What speech?"

"The one about my duty to humanity. It comes in two phases and many textures. Phase one has to do with my duty to humanity and really means we could make a classic buck with it. Phase two deals solely with my duty to humanity, and I don't hear that one very often. Phase two utterly overlooks the reluctance humanity has to accept good things unless they arrive from accepted and respectable sources. Phase one is fully aware of this but gets very rat-shrewd in figuring ways around it."

She said, "I don't—" but could get no farther.

"The textures," he overrode her, "are accompanied by the

light of revelation, with or without religion and/or mysticism; or they are cast sternly in the ethical-philosophy mold and aim to force me to surrender through guilt mixed, to some degree all the way up to total, with compassion."

"But I only—"

"You," he said, aiming a long index finger at her, "have robbed yourself of the choicest example of everything I have just said. If my assumptions had been right and you had gone to your friendly local sawbones, and he had diagnosed cancer and referred you to a specialist, and he had done likewise and sent you to a colleague for consultation, and in random panic you had fallen into my hands and been cured, and had gone back to your various doctors to report a miracle, do you know what you'd have gotten from them? 'Spontaneous remission,' that's what you'd have gotten. And it wouldn't be only doctors," he went on with a sudden renewal of passion, under which she quailed in her bed. "Everybody has his own commercial. Your nutritionist would have nodded over his wheat germ or his macrobiotic rice cakes, your priest would have dropped to his knees and looked at the sky, your geneticist would have a pet theory about generation skipping and would assure you that your grandparents probably had spontaneous remissions too and never knew it."

"Please!" she cried, but he shouted at her: "Do you know what I am? I am an engineer twice over, mechanical and electrical, and I have a law degree. If you were foolish enough to tell anyone about what has happened here (which I hope you aren't, but if you are I know how to protect myself) I could be jailed for practicing medicine without a license, you could have me up for assault because I stuck a needle into you and even for kidnapping if you could prove I carried you in here from the lab. Nobody would give a damn that I had cured your cancer. You don't know who I am, do you?"

"No, I don't even know your name."

"And I won't tell you. I don't know your name, either—"

"Oh! It's—"

"Don't tell me! Don't tell me! I don't want to hear it! I

wanted to be involved with your lump and I was. I want it and you to be gone as soon as you're both up to it. Have I made myself absolutely clear?"

"Just let me get dressed," she said tightly, "and I'll leave right now!"

"Without making a speech?"

"Without making a speech." And in a flash her anger turned to misery and she added, "I was going to say I was grateful. Would that have been all right?"

And his anger underwent a change too, for he came close to the bed and sat down on his heel, bringing their faces to a level, and said quite gently, "That would be fine. Although . . . you won't really be grateful for another ten days, when you get your 'spontaneous remission' reports, or maybe for six months or a year or two or five, when examinations keep on testing out negative."

She detected such a wealth of sadness behind this that she found herself reaching for the hand with which he steadied himself against the edge of the bed. He did not recoil, but he didn't seem to welcome it either. "Why can't I be grateful right now?"

"That would be an act of faith," he said bitterly, "and that just doesn't happen any more—if it ever did." He rose and went toward the door. "Please don't go tonight," he said. "It's dark and you don't know the way. I'll see you in the morning."

When he came back in the morning the door was open. The bed was made and the sheets were folded neatly on the chair, together with the pillow slips and the towels she had used. She wasn't there.

He came out into the entrance court and contemplated his bonsai.

Early sun gold-frosted the horizontal upper foliage of the old tree and brought its gnarled limbs into sharp relief, tough brown-gray and crevices of velvet. Only the companion of a bonsai (there are owners of bonsai, but they are a lesser breed) fully understands the relationship. There is an exclusive and individual treeness to the tree because it is a living thing, and living things change, and there are definite ways in which the tree desires to change. A man sees the tree and in his mind makes certain extensions and extrapolations of what he sees, and sets about making them happen. The tree in turn will do only what a tree can do, will resist to the death any attempt to do what it cannot do, or to do it in less time than it needs. The shaping of a bonsai is therefore always a compromise and always a cooperation. A man cannot create bonsai, nor can a tree; it takes both, and they must understand each other. It takes a long time to do that. One memorizes one's bonsai, every twig, the angle of every crevice and needle, and, lying awake at night or in a pause a thousand miles away, one recalls this or that line or mass, one makes one's plans. With wire and water and light, with tilting and with the planting of water-robbing weeds or heavy root-shading ground cover, one explains to the tree what one wants, and if the explanation is well enough made, and there is great enough understanding, the tree will respond and obey—almost. Always there will be its own self-respecting, highly individual variation: *Very well, I shall do what you want, but I will do it* my *way.* And for these variations, the tree is always willing to present a clear and logical explanation, and more often than not (almost smiling) it will make clear to the man that he could have avoided it if his understanding had been better.

It is the slowest sculpture in the world, and there is, at times, doubt as to which is being sculpted, man or tree.

So he stood for perhaps ten minutes watching the flow of gold over the upper branches, and then went to a carved wooden chest, opened it, shook out a length of disreputable cotton duck, opened the hinged glass at one side of the atrium, and spread the canvas over the roots and all the earth to one side of the trunk, leaving the rest open to wind and water. Perhaps in a while—a month or two—a certain shoot in the topmost branch would take the hint, and the uneven flow of moisture up through the cambium layer would nudge it away from that upward reach and persuade it to continue the horizontal passage. And perhaps not, and it would need the harsher language of binding and wire. But then it might have something to say, too, about the rightness of an upward trend, and would perhaps say it persuasively enough to convince the man; altogether, a patient, meaningful, and rewarding dialogue.

"Good morning."

"Oh goddam!" he barked, "you made me bite my tongue. I thought you'd gone."

"I did." She knelt in the shadows with her back against the inner wall, facing the atrium. "But then I stopped to be with the tree for a while."

"Then what?"

"I thought a lot."

"What about?"

"You."

"Did you now!"

"Look," she said firmly, "I'm not goint to any doctor to get this thing checked out. I didn't want to leave until I had told you that, and until I was sure you believed me."

"Come on in and we'll get something to eat."

Foolishly, she giggled. "I can't. My feet are asleep."

Without hesitation he scooped her up in his arms and carried her around the atrium. She said, her arm around his shoulders and their faces close, "Do you believe me?"

He continued around until they reached the wooden chest, then stopped and looked into her eyes. "I believe you. I don't know why you decided that, but I'm willing to believe you." He set her down on the chest and stood back.

"It's that act of faith you mentioned," she said gravely. "I thought you ought to have it, at least once in your life, so you can never say such a thing again." She tapped her heels gingerly against the slate floor. "Ow." She made a pained smile. "Pins and needles."

"You must have been thinking for a long time."

90

"Yes. Want more?"

"Sure."

"You are an angry, frightened man."

He seemed delighted. "Tell me about all that!"

"No," she said quietly, "you tell me. I'm very serious about this. Why are you angry?"

"I'm not!"

"Why are you so angry?"

"I tell you I'm not! Although," he added good-naturedly, "you're pushing me in that direction."

"Well then, why?"

He gazed at her for what, to her, seemed a very long time indeed. "You really want to know, don't you?"

She nodded.

He waved a sudden hand, up and out. "Where do you suppose all this came from—the house, the land, the equipment?"

She waited.

"An exhaust system," he said, with a thickening of the voice she was coming to know. "A way of guiding exhaust gases out of internal-combustion engines in such a way that they are given a spin. Unburned solids are embedded in the walls of the muffler in a glass-wool liner that slips out in one piece and can be replaced by a clean one every couple of thousand miles. The rest of the exhaust is fired by its own spark plug and what will burn, burns. The heat is used to preheat the fuel; the rest is spun again through a five-thousand-mile cartridge. What finally gets out is, by today's standards at least, pretty clean; and because of the preheating, it actually gets better mileage out of the engine."

"So you've made a lot of money."

"I made a lot of money," he echoed. "But not because the thing is being used to cut down air pollution. I got the money because an automobile company bought it and buried it in a lock-box. They don't like it because it costs something to install in new cars. Some friends of theirs in the refining business don't like it because it gets high performance out of crude fuels. Well all right—I didn't know any better and I won't make the same mistake again. But yes—I'm angry. I was angry when I was a kid on a tankship and we were set to washing down bulkhead with chipped brown-soap and canvas, and I went ashore and bought a detergent and tried it and it was better, faster and cheaper so I took it to the bos'n, who gave me a punch in the mouth for pretending to know his job better than he did . . . well, he was drunk at the time, but the rough part was when the old shellbacks in the crew got wind of it and ganged up on me for being what they called a 'company man'—that's a dirty name in a ship. I just couldn't understand why people got in the way of something better.

"I've been up against that all my life. I have something in my head that just won't quit: it's a way I have of asking the next question: Why is so-and-so the way it is? Why can't it be such-and-such instead? There is always another question to be asked about any thing or any situation; especially you shouldn't quit when you like an answer because there's always another one after it. And we live in a world where people just don't want to ask the next question!

"I've been paid all my stomach will take for things people won't use, and if I'm mad all the time it's really my fault—I admit it; because I just can't stop asking that next question and coming up with answers. There's a half-dozen real blockbusters in that lab that nobody will ever see, and half a hundred more in my head; but what can you do in a world where people would rather kill each other in a desert even when they're shown it can turn green and bloom, where they'll fall all over themselves to pour billions into developing a new oil strike when it's been proved over and over again that the fossil fuels will kill us all?

"Yes, I'm angry. Shouldn't I be?"

She let the echoes of his voice swirl around the court and out through the hole in the top of the atrium, and waited a little longer to let him know he was here with her and not beside himself and his fury. He grinned at her sheepishly when he came to this, and she said:

"Maybe you're asking the next question instead of asking the right question. I think people who live by wise old sayings are trying not to think, but I know one worth paying some attention to. It's this: If you ask a question the right way, you've just given the answer." She paused to see if he was paying real attention. He was. She went on, "I mean, if you put your hand on a hot stove you might ask yourself, how can I stop my hand from burning? And the answer is pretty clear, isn't it? If the world keeps rejecting what you have to give, there's some way of asking why that contains the answer."

"It's a simple answer," he said shortly. "People are stupid."

"That isn't the answer and you know it," she said.

"What is?"

"Oh, I can't tell you that! All I know is that the way you do something, when people are concerned, is more important than what you do, if you want results. I mean . . . you already know how to get what you want with the tree, don't you?"

"I'll be damned."

"People are living growing things too. I don't know a hundredth part of what you do about bonsai, but I do know this: when you start one, it isn't often the strong straight healthy ones you take. It's the twisted sick ones that can be made the most beautiful. When you get to shaping humanity, you might remember that."

"Of all the—I don't know whether to laugh in your face or punch you right in the mouth!"

She rose. He hadn't realized she was quite this tall. "I'd better go."

"Come on now. You know a figure of speech when you hear one."

"Oh, I didn't feel threatened. But—I'd better go, all the same."

Shrewdly, he asked her, "Are you afraid to ask the next question?"

"Terrified."

"Ask it anyway."

"No!"

"Then I'll do it for you. You said I was angry—and afraid. You want to know what I'm afraid of."

"Yes."

"You. I am scared to death of you."

"Are you really?"

"You have a way of provoking honesty," he said with some difficulty. "I'll say what I know you're thinking: I'm afraid of any close human relationship. I'm afraid of something I can't take apart with a screwdriver or a mass spectroscope or a table of cosines and tangents." His voice was jocular but his hands were shaking.

"You do it by watering one side," she said softly, "or by turning it just so in the sun. You handle it as if it were a living thing, like a species or a woman or a bonsai. It will be what you want it to be if you let it be itself and take the time and the care."

"I think," he said, "that you are making me some kind of offer. Why?"

"Sitting there most of the night," she said, "I had a crazy kind of image. Do you think two sick twisted trees ever made bonsai out of one another?"

"What's your name?" he asked her.

It's You!

"It's you!"

It wasn't the hair that made him cry out like that, though God knows California's enough to turn anyone into a hair freak these days; well she was enough by herself with that silken waterfall of coppery-canary to freak you, and it wasn't that or the crinkle-cornered arch on arch of the eye and brow or the perfect teeth, not by themselves. It wasn't even the absolute confidence with which she wore the see-through shirt through which he saw the absolute confidence of her breasts, or even that she was exactly tall enough and round enough. More than anything else, it was that she was real.

Everybody does this thing, although some cats know it more than others: you see chicks, you see pix, you add and subtract and over the years things settle in—just so big, just so dark, just so—just exactly so until it's all finished. Then that finished thing, that *her,* settles down inside you and every time you see someone, or in a magazine, or at the show, you set it up against *her.* It could be great, you could get excited, you could dream a lot about any of the others, but somehow they never, never check out with the *her* you've made.

So when he saw her he yelled it out. It came out of him and he hadn't known he was going to say it, it hit him that hard. Maybe that's how you know—it bursts out of you without a thought.

He'd just parked the Monster and was half in, half out when he saw her. She was hitchhiking with a girl friend—they do that a lot in California. He was never able to remember much about that girlfriend, Susie or Dottie or something. Maybe he never saw her, much. There was this truck parked off the road with berries and corn-on-the-cob and tomatoes and stuff, and he liked corn and that was why he stopped. He walked over to the two girls and pointed at the Monster and said, "I'll be right with you." They smiled at him and looked him over, and at each other, checking him out, and then said Thanks and went over to the car. Something developed fists inside his chest and began hitting him from inside so hard he blinked with each beat. He went over to the truck and bought corn, a couple of ears. He lived by himself.

But before he picked it up he went back to the Monster. They'd got themselves somehow into the one bucket seat. He asked her, "Do you like corn?" She said she did. He went back and got a couple more and some tomatoes and a cantelope, and then he saw the stocks, long clusters of white and purple flowers with a heavy scent that nobody's ever put in a bottle yet. He bought one white bunch and one purple and mixed them together right there into one big bunch, and he had never done anything like that in his life before.

They went first to the girlfriend's house. Without remembering the girlfriend much, he long remembered the thick waves of disapproval she set up when she got out and the other one, *her,* didn't. It made him laugh when he pulled away from the curb and they were alone together, and he met her eyes and she was laughing too.

She lived in Altadena, which was a hell of a haul away from where he lived, but he didn't mind. Oh, he didn't mind. She lived in a little two-room guest house the other side of a swimming pool; the people in the big house hardly ever used it. It had its own little driveway. It was nice. She said she would cook the corn for him. She did, with some lamb chops he had in the freezer, and they ate the cantelope with vanilla ice cream on it and a pinch of dry instant coffee sprinkled on it. She could cook. You could tell. There were more than forty herbs and spices in the kitchen. She made up a name for him, Knightly. She said he looked like a knight in shining armor. He never did call her by her name, except sometimes Hon.

It was one of those hot smoggy California evenings and the pool looked good, but he didn't have a suit. She laughed at him and said who needs it? When she peeled off the see-through top he saw it wasn't a see-through at all, no more than a stained-glass window is a see-through when you want to look at the sun. There can't be a more perfect body than that one, not anywhere, not only for the perfection of each part, but for the absolute rightness of a breast like that with a shoulder like that, and a waist that turned just so together with such slender ankles. Also, all her hair was that same yellowy-coppery color and there wasn't a flaw on her skin anywhere.

They fell into the pool and laughed a lot, and you are not going to believe this easily but it's true: there was something about the way she did it all, something about the way she was, that made him not touch her then. They dried off on some of a mountain of thick clean towels she had and got dressed again and he never made the first pass. Maybe it was because passes often get made because a guy just has to find out where it's at, and in this case he knew where it was at. They both knew. It happened later, much later, about two in the morning, after which (it was pretty wonderful) she said softly "Knightly-night" and fell asleep in his arms. He didn't go home until Saturday.

On the way back to his place he stopped at a Rents and hired a 6-by-10 trailer. They had a hell of a job rigging a hitch for it on the Monster without bashing those beautiful chrome pipes, and it took a half hour to figure a way to get the big right-hand rearview mounted, and when he took off he was one hell of a sight. It was like a racehorse hitched to a manure spreader and people all over stopped in their tracks to watch him go by, and he was sure that one sideswipe on the freeway was caused by some yokel rubbernecking him. At his place he loaded on everything he owned, which wasn't really too much. He was paid till the end of the month but screw it. He took it all out to the guest house in Altadena.

She was supposed to clear out the second room for him but when he got there she had rearranged the whole house so that there was a real living room and a real bedroom instead of the overlap she'd had before. There was plenty of room in the closet for his clothes—more than he needed—but she'd fixed up everything else so perfectly that there was really no place to put anything of his, and anyway, who needed it? It was an Our House.

He was on Emergency then, which had always suited him fine. He was one of those lucky people who went to sleep bang whenever he felt tired, and could wake up—all the way up—in twenty minutes or two hours or ten, whatever was handy, and any part of the twenty-four was all right with him. She was a day people, however, and midnight was late to her always, and 8 A.M. was late too. She liked to be up before seven. He adjusted to that pretty well, and also learned not to talk when she was going through the complicated secret ritual of getting to sleep. Some people are like that. They have to do whatever it is they do to get to sleep, everything in the right order and skipping none of it, and if you interrupt, they have to go back to the beginning and start over. She wouldn't sleep late, not ever, so when he'd kept her up late she looked drawn and kind of sad all the next day and evening. He also found out she would go to sleep almost instantly after sex, when it was good, and it was almost always good. But the whole sleep thing was hard to handle while he was on Emergency and would get calls at two and three in the morning and get out and not know when he'd be back. She was sweet about it—she was sweet about everything—but after awhile he put in for the day shift. It meant a little less money, but what the hell.

He quit going to Mother's, which believe it or not is a chain of pool halls in the L.A. area. Nobody said he couldn't, but pool or snooker just wasn't her thing, and when he played with her sitting patiently smiling in the front of the place and waiting for him to get done, it wasn't the same. She was nice as could be to Scruffy and Ralph and Rod and the rest, and even the Blinker, even though she didn't dig him. Well, you had to know the Blinker. And the way she did it was great, warm and lively with all of them but there was never any doubt as to whose girl she was and meant to be. But . . . it wasn't the same, and pretty soon he went less and less and didn't see the herd at Mother's any more. Likewise the hangarounds at Butch's Aircooled, except when something on the Monster needed fixing, which wasn't often. Once when he went down for new connectors on his tach he found himself taking an hour instead of ten minutes to put them in, and driving away he felt a single wild strong tug inside him that he just couldn't understand. Well they were just a bunch of greasy cats who couldn't talk or think anything but chops and cams and pots and mags and slicks, but . . . .

In the first couple of days she gave him a medallion on a chain around his neck, a funny little twist of silver with a flat piece of fire opal on it, and he wore it night and day. For a long time he wore it swinging outside and was glad to say "My chick," when someone asked about it.

His subscriptions to *Car and Driver* and *Road and Track* got screwed up somehow and six weeks went by and he didn't even miss them. You have to know him to know what that really meant. He was very content. He'd tell her that every once in a while just to see her light up. He told himself that too. He bought the magazines at the newsstand and when the next issues came out she threw away the old ones. He was a little shook, and although he didn't say anything, he kept the magazines at work after that.

One morning the alarm went off and he rolled out and fumbled for his clothes and they felt different. Instead of the black tight cords and the Western shirt with the rawhide on the pockets, there were a pair of black jeans, real tailored, with slightly bell bottoms and a dark dull kind of paisley print shirt with a scarf and ring attached to it. They were really cool and he liked them but he said hell, he couldn't go to work in them, he'd look like a peacock. She lay in the bed watching him with a say-you-like-them, pent-up joy on her face. She'd made them herself secretly whenever she could snatch the time when he wasn't around, and kept hiding the pieces before he came back until they were all done. So he said what she wanted to hear and he did wear them to work that once, although he wore the medallion inside his shirt instead of outside. Sure enough the crew gave him a rough time about it and when he came home he said he'd save the bells and the paisley for parties, they were too good to risk at work. And he got to the trash before they collected it and found his black cords and Western shirt and put them away in the garage in a box with the rest of his stuff still out there. He never knew why and nobody asked him but he wore the medallion inside his shirt after that.

She made him three more pairs of pants and two more shirts, and they were really great, but for parties. They'd go to parties, people she'd known a long time. They were okay parties. He never liked drinking much but he'd drink a little sometimes and like it a little, and he could take pot or leave it alone. Only sometimes after a party where he had laughed a lot, he would leave with a strange feeling that he had just crossed a desert. It could be full of people but there just wasn't anybody to talk to. One time he parked outside one of the parties and there in the dark under a tree was a silver Excalibur. He always said an Excalibur was a piece of candy, but secretly he thought it was a whole big heap of wheels, and if anybody ever offered to swap him for the Monster he'd keep the Monster, but he sure would think it over a lot. So when they got inside he made it his business to find out who was driving it, and he had his mouth all set to sit down and really talk, but it turned out to belong to some rich chick whose daddy had given it to her for her eighteenth birthday and she didn't know an axle from an ax handle. That one time he really felt cheated and mad, and it was the first time he felt dead sure he couldn't explain it and drove home too fast without talking and scared her a bit, and wouldn't talk after they got home either.

Also she cut his hair. She could do that. She could do anything she tried, and she did it well. It looked great. It was a lot different but it really did look fine.

One night after some sex, and it really was the most, and she slipped off to sleep in the way she had, he lay thinking about things and remembered something about rollbars and anti-sways he had read somewhere, but couldn't pin it down. He got up carefully and went out to the Monster and got the flashlight and went into the garage and got out the boxes with the back issues in them, and squatted there looking them over for so long his feet went numb and the batteries quit. He sat there in the dark banging his heels against the concrete to wake them up and you know something? he felt wonderful. He put away the magazines in the boxes and then put away the boxes and limped back into the house and to bed. He didn't think she knew.

He bought heavy-duty batteries first thing next day, and about a week later it happened again just the same way. He didn't figure out what was happening—he was not the figuring-out kind, maybe. But the third or fourth time it happened he was kneeling in the middle of the concrete floor with a drag pictorial on steam turbines down at the bottom of his tunnel of light when he heard something. He switched off his flash and the color print of a bright red three-wheel squirt, with the driver in prone position, faded from his eyes to be replaced by her shadowy naked figure in the doorway.

He said, "Well, I didn't want you to wake up."

She said the only bitter thing she had ever said to him. She pointed at his crotch and said, "You use that as a kind of sleeping pill for me, don't you?" Then she went back inside.

He stayed to pack away the magazines and then followed. She seemed to be asleep so he got in quietly and did not touch her. They did not talk about it in the morning.

That night they went to another party, and no less than

three cats told him at different times how great his threads were. Well, she had good taste, she knew what looked good. The party was beautiful people and two guitars and a side table full of things made of rice and a lot of different kinds of cheese and wine—a desert. When they got home she went to bed and he went into the bathroom to get rid of the desert inside and out, and a terrible thing happened to him. He looked into the mirror and did not know who that was in there.

I mean it was a great haircut and the guru-style collar on the cotton-satin shirt-jacket was so well-cut it did not look freaky, and then there were the deep-buffed reversed-calf boots, like suede so nappy it was almost fur. But none of it was *him,* nothing he remembered, nothing he ever thought about when he thought *Me.* A terrible thing.

He took off all the clothes and hung them up and put them and the shoes away. Then he took off the medallion and put it on the TV and went to bed and right to sleep.

She was up ahead of him as usual and breakfast was ready. He went out into the garage naked and found his black cords and the Western shirt with the rawhide on the pockets, and his old lineman's boots, and put them all on. He came in and ate. While he was eating she told him she had done everything in the world to make him happy. He agreed that she had and said it had all been great.

It was Saturday and he hopped in the Monster and went down to the Rents. He felt very strange, holding something inside of himself locked down tight, knowing it was no good to let it all out because he couldn't explain it to anybody if he did. They remembered him all right and got the 6-by-10 hitched on and the mirror mounted in half the time. He drove back to the house and up the driveway to the garage and loaded all his stuff into the trailer. It didn't take too long.

She came out and watched him finish. "Come inside."

He just shook his head and vaulted into the bucket. She came over and stood beside the Monster, holding her hands together real tight. "Knightly, Knightly, what is it? Tell me what's the matter."

He could only stare blindly at the tachometer. The only thing that came to him seemed so crazy he could not bring himself to say it: *I want my real name back.* He said, "I'm no good at explaining things, Hon."

But she was. She knelt by the Monster so he could look down into those double-arched eyes in that frame of coppery-yellow, and she said how she had been thinking and thinking, and she realized how wrong she had been. She began a whole list of promises. She said, "I'll try to learn about cars and go with you to the dragstrips and the shops. I'll pick it up quickly, and then I'll pay more attention to the way you want to look and not the way I want you to look. And I never realized it but I shouldn't've made you quit the Emergency and live the way I live." And more, like about she never had found out what he used to eat before he met her, she just cooked what she thought he ought to like without asking. She would change, she would change. Any way he wanted her to, she would change.

He almost had a thought worth saying, something about what happened to people when they had to change, but he couldn't get it into shape. Maybe later she could figure it out for herself. He started the motor and shifted into low and checked the mirrors on both sides, and then throttled way back so she could hear him. He said, as he began slipping the clutch, "It ain't any of those things, Hon.

"It's you."

Take Care Of Joey

Talking to this bartender, I forget what about, he said wait and reached for the backbar phone. I hadn't much noticed the little guy in the green sweater but he had. He was eyeing him while he dialed so I did too. The little guy was ambling down the whole length of the place and slowing down, not quite stopping, at each bar stool. Every customer got the eye, a cold, up-down and back kind of hit-me-why-doncha look. Spooky. Some little guys got this banty-cock thing going: you know, I'm little but I'm tough, try me out, and they really are tough. This one wasn't. Somehow his legs didn't work right, I can't say how, it wasn't even a limp, and he was real skinny.

"Hello, Dwight. This is Danny at the Ramble Inn. Joey just come in and it looks like he— Yeah. Yeah. Yeah." He hung up and the both of us watched this little guy, this Joey. Some of the customers turned their back, swing to the left as he come near, swing to the right as he passed, and when that happened he would edge in next to them and hang there until they had to face him. He'd give them that eye and like twitch his upper lip at one side and if they didn't say nothing he would walk on, and they didn't say nothing.

Then some others would look at him what-the-hell, and he would look right back at them until they turned away, and then move on. One customer, he was a big guy and kind of sleepy-looking, but look out for guys like that, he said "You want something?" and this little Joey waits a good long time to answer him, "Maybe later." Then there's me, because I'm down at the bottom end with the bartender. I'm watching him in the mirror by then and he can't know that, so he stands by my elbow doing nothing so long I got to turn around and look at him. I said Hi.

He didn't say nothing. He waited what got to be an awful long time, hanging those boiled-looking eyes on me, and then he spit on the floor. I didn't have to move my feet, but almost. He kept on looking and then rounded me and said to the bartender "I want to make a boiler."

Danny the bartender got him his shot and chaser and the little guy took the glasses and moved over to a table where he could see everybody. I said, "Guy like that, could be trouble."

"Will be trouble," Danny the bartender says.

Before I can talk any more there comes in a tall man, worried, looked all around but I don't think he could see this Joey because he come straight down to where I am and says to the bartender, "Danny, where. . . ."

"Hi, Dwight. There he is." He points with his eyes.

Dwight, that's the tall one, he flashes a look and then uses the backbar mirror to study out this Joey, seems like he wants to know everything he can by looking without talking to him. I seen him squinch up his face when Joey knocks back the rye and chugalugs his chaser. I hear him say O God when Joey gets up.

Joey puts a cigarette in his chops and kind of sets his chin down and moves halfway up the bar where sits this big sleepy-looking guy who told him before, "You want something?" and he reaches for the guy's cigar which is in a ashtray on the bar. Dwight says in my ear again O God and Danny the bartender says "Dwight, you better get him out of here." and Sleepy says "Hey get your goddam hands off my *see*gar."

Joey goes right on getting a light off the cigar for his

cigarette and paying no mind and Dwight starts moving up toward the two of them and maybe it would of been all right even then but Joey taken the cigar and dropped it in the big guy's highball. Well of course that was it and Sleepy takes a swing but by that time Dwight is there in between them and more than that—he gives little Joey a shoulder that sends him cakewalking back out of the way. For that Dwight has to take the punch on the side of his neck and he puts up his hands like peacemaking and says Cool it or some such.

But Sleepy is not about to cool it now and gets on his feet, and he is a much bigger man than I thought. He winds up a ham-handed right at the end of an arm like a tree-trunk, and I have seen guys who do that and I want to yell at Dwight don't pay no attention to that big looping windup, he wants you to, and sure enough Sleepy's left comes out from under his armpit traveling short and straight and lays Dwight out flat on the floor and sliding.

Disgusted and scared I hear Danny the bartender say "God now I got to call the pleece, I hate to call the pleece," so I told him not to and went up there where the trouble was, Dwight wiggling a little on the floor and Sleepy with his eye on Joey and Joey backing away. I guess I was going to try to talk it through but Sleepy tromps Dwight. He does it still looking at Joey like he don't care where he tromps him and he don't, either. I don't like guys who tromp guys unless they need to, so I told Sleepy to quit and he tromped Dwight again looking at me now and cocking that big phony right-hander my way, and when you see them do that twice in a row you know you got a one-trick fighter, which makes it easy for anyone who knows two, and I know half a hundred.

I showed him some and he never laid a hand on me but the one I grabbed the wrist of and rolled him over my back and airplaned him, and by that time I had got to him four times already and he wasn't about to get up again for a while. I got Dwight up on his feet and over to where my drink was and he hung onto the bar shaking his head. Danny the bartender give him a shot and that seemed to help a little while the customers went back to their stools except a couple over to see about Sleepy. I called over to them not to worry. And meanwhile that little Joey that started it all is standing right where he was where Sleepy had pushed him to.

Danny said for me to drink my drink. "It's on the house, grateful, but get that Joey out of here, he's bad news from now on out, I know him, honest to God, Dwight"—and I realized it was Dwight he was talking to now not me—"I don't know why you do it. If it was me I would just let somebody plow him under."

Dwight says "Well it ain't you. Thanks for the drink." He looks at me and he thanks me too. I said I'll go along with him. Sometimes when these things happen they are not finished where they start and you get jumped outside. Dwight said he didn't think so this time and neither did I but I went anyway. We kind of collected Joey one on each side walking out. He went right along with it, he held back only a second at the door to look back where a couple of guys was helping Sleepy onto his feet, and then he looked at Dwight, and then he laughed at him. He didn't pay no attention to me at all. I mean he was a very creepy little guy.

I went along with them and I will tell you why. I have seen a lot in a lot of places, and there is one thing that always hooks me and that is when I see somebody taking care of somebody, because to tell you the truth I just can not understand it. Why a guy throws his self on a grenade to save other guys. Why some stranger runs into a burning house to get someone out. How it is you can call somebody up in the middle of the night and he will run out to get some other guy out of trouble. You can say all you want about heroes and survival of the race and sacrifice and all like that, and I say bullshit. Maybe you want to believe that stuff but what I believe is that people is either wolves or wolverines when they are not tapeworms or sheep, and that is that.

All the same I keep looking, I really don't know why. I look very hard and I don't like it. I mean it's like I don't want to find out even once that anyone would really and truly take care of someone else without he got something out of it. It's like I'm scared to find it out, like my whole world would get shook upside down if I ever did, but I keep looking.

The first thing happened when we left the Ramble Inn was Joey pulled away from us and run straight out into the street. There was cars coming and a truck and a bus and Joey just did not seem to give a damn. There was a lot of honking and screeching and cussing right away and Dwight, he was still rocking from that powerhouse punch, but all the same he dove out into that traffic and got to Joey and throwed both arms around him and rassled him to the dotted line between lanes and held him there until the traffic opened up and he could shove him back to the sidewalk. He was cussing him out too and he meant it. Joey just laughed. Dwight told him to get the hell home before somebody killed him, and I think he really meant himself, him, Dwight, was the somebody. Joey just said Nope. He still did not pay any attention to me.

Dwight turned the little guy loose and he started to amble down the street and Dwight walked slow behind him. He kept his eyes on him almost every second. He said to me well, thanks for what you done in there, it was like good-bye, beat it. But I walked along with him. So after a while Dwight said he could handle things all right. He said, "He gets like this every once in a while, wants to go out and drink. It is not too hard as long as you keep your eye on him and head him off from the big ones." I don't think he meant big guys, I think he meant big trouble.

I said if he didn't mind me asking, when a guy is so eager to get his self killed, why not just let him do it? because he sure is asking for it. And Dwight said "No he's not." He said that positive, I mean like he *knew*.

So there was Joey walking along in the middle of the night like he wasn't going no place in particular and didn't much care, and the two of us following along a little way behind watching him and talking a little once in a while. When I kept on sticking around, Dwight quit saying thanks-and-goodnight things. I found out they were not related, they did not come from the same town, they did not live together or work in the same company or even in the same line. Dwight was a shop foreman, I think in some kind of printing place, he was a pretty educated guy, I mean you got the idea he could go a lot farther if something wasn't holding him back. Joey was a sheet metal man in a auto body place. Also they were not queer. The more I found out about them the more worried I got that here was somebody who was ready to lay it on the line for somebody else without any payoff, none at all. I mean, I don't think they even liked each other.

So I finally asked him right out, why? and all he said was, "There's some things you just got to do."

Then Joey began to run.

You wouldn't believe a spindly little guy like that could take off that way, one second ambling along looking into store windows, the next scooting like a squirted apple seed. I heard that same tired O God from Dwight, and then voom he's off after the little guy. I thought well hell, and went after them.

Joey went straight for three blocks widening the gap all the way. I right away dug that Dwight was not in good shape at all because when I passed him in the first half-block he was already wheezing for breath. So I did not bother with him but made it my business to round up that Joey and nail him down good. It was not easy.

He turned right into an alley and if I had not really been pushing myself I would not of seen him turn right again into a dead-end loading area behind a big warehouse. It was dark in there but not altogether. All the same I could not see him any place.

I backed away looking every place until I was in the alley again so Dwight would see me when he come by, and he did. He was so pooped and tuckered and winded out he could not talk at all, and when I told him which way Joey had went he just nodded his head and hung on to a brick wall gasping and coughing a little once in a while until he was put together again. Then he said, "We got to stop him now. He got something wrong with his heart muscle, he shouldn't run like that. He knows that but he does it every once in a while anyway the dirty rotten little son of a bitch." So now I knew it wasn't just not liking each other, Dwight, he hated that little guy.

He went back into the loading area and looked all around. Somebody told me once that if you ever want to hide, don't go down or behind, go up. Guys looking for something will always look down or under or behind things, never up unless something attracts them. I remembered that and so started looking up, and sure enough.

I hit on Dwight's arm and pointed. There was a fire escape that went clear up to the roof and about sixty feet up there was a black blob kind of weaving back and forth. If you looked real careful you could see it was Joey, and after a while you could see he was on one of the landings of the steel stairway, and when your eyes got really used to it you could see he was at the end of the landing on the wrong side of the railing, hanging on to it and standing on one leg and pivoting back and forth, hanging out over nothing at all.

"O God. I got to get him. He gets dizzy spells." Dwight started to run for the bottom of the ladder. I got to him in two jumps. It was easy, he did not have his breath back even yet. I said how the hell did he think he was going to get to the ladder?

It was one of those swing-down ladders that if you are on the fire escape coming down you get on it and it comes down, otherwise it stays up on the second floor level so burglars can't get to use it. Somebody must of tied it down and Joey found it like that, he sure did not leave it like that. You would have to be a bird or a polevaulter to get to it now. And up there Joey was swinging like a monkey, I heard him laugh.

Dwight got right under the ladder and jumped. It was pathetic. He jumped and jumped, I think he was more than half out of his mind. "We got to get to him," I think he was saying over and over in between those little tired useless jumps—you could not tell he was so out of breath.

There was a smooth six-inch pipe at the corner of the building running from the ground up to the third floor, I don't know why. It passed about four feet away from that second-floor landing of the fire escape where the swing-down ladder was. From the ground it looked like a long way up and a hell of a way from the landing, and a smooth six-inch pipe is not the easiest thing to get hold of but what the hell. I started up it hand over hand. There wasn't nothing feet could do so I just let them hang there and come along for the ride. Down below me Dwight was trying to follow me, he could not even get off the ground.

When I got above the landing I stopped for a couple seconds to get my breath because a couple of seconds was all my hands had left in them. I flipped my feet up and out to get a swing, swung back and then forward and let go, trying to shove at the same time. It was a nice idea but it did not altogether work. I did not get both hands on the guard rail as I figured; I got one hand on the flat floor-bars. It hurt a whole lot but I could hang on until I stopped swinging and was able to climb to the landing. I had to lay down for quite a time before I was ready to move on.

I guess I could of pushed the ladder down then and let Dwight take over but tell you the truth I never thought of it. I started up after that crazy Joey.

I heard him laughing again.

I went up kind of on all fours. I think he thought it was Dwight, not me. Anyway when I got to the sixth landing he started to scream at me, "You ain't Dwight, you get the hell out of here, you mind your own goddam business, it's old Dwight'll take care of me." I did not say nothing but kept on coming. He was still over the rail leaning back against his grip. All he had to do was open his fingers and that was it. I came on slow.

Maybe it was all fun for him up to then, I don't know. Maybe it was getting mad at me like that, that made some difference inside his crazy head. But as I come close I could see in the little bit of stray light his eyes go funny. I mean he stopped screaming and he stopping swinging and his eyes went white, I guess they rolled right on up out of sight. And his knees started to buckle.

I jumped. I reached for him with my right hand because I am right-handed and because I did not have no time to think. It was the same hand I caught myself with when I swung off the pipe and it was bloody and skinned. It hurt a whole lot but that was all right—it just wouldn't work very good. It landed into his armpit as he fell, which is a hell of a way to catch anybody, and got hold of a bunch of shirt and skin. I fell down and slid forward and he would of pulled me right off after him but I arched my back and caught the underside of the rail with my heels. As long as I could keep my knees bent my heels made a sort of half-ass hook that at least stopped the sliding. I got my other hand on him. He was no help, he was dead weight, he was out cold. I remember thinking to myself for just one second, oh the hell with it, I've done enough. But I did not listen to that and I hung on, and after a minute I found the strength to pull him up high enough to bend his chest onto the deck bars and press back and fall full length on them and pull him all the way in.

Way down below in the dark Dwight was yelling and yelling something. He was yelling, "Don't hit him. For God's sake don't hit him."

I think if he had not passed out like that I would of hit him. Like I said I know a lot of tricks but there are some I know I never got to try yet and I would of liked to try some of them out. But there wasn't any need, and after I rested I hung him on my shoulder and walked down the fire escape with him. The swinging ladder went down without no trouble and I got to the ground and it swung up again with a clang and I put Joey down on the ground.

Dwight jumped on him and felt him all over and put his ear on Joey's mouth and lit a match and rolled back an eyelid and then he hunkered down and pulled a deep sigh. "He's going to be all right."

I said that was a damn shame.

Dwight said he would lay like this for a half hour or so and then come to, and he would take him home. He said then he probably would not pull anything like this again for two, three weeks.

I think I got a little bit mad then and I called him a number of names all meaning Stupid. I said to waste his time looking out for a crazy ugly little fart like that Joey, he should have his head candled.

He hunkered there by Joey and looked up at me and let me run down and then he said well, he guessed I had the right to hear the whole story.

He said there's always one kid in any crowd that is the goat for everybody—the little fat boy. Or sometimes the little skinny boy or the one boy with curly hair. He said the more everybody jumps on that one kid the more you get to hate him, and sometimes it does you good to get him alone and beat the hell out of him just because he is there to beat the hell out of. So Joey was that kid, see, and one day Dwight got him alone and beat the hell out of him, and Joey got up off the ground and hit him. Maybe it was just he was not ready, but he went over like tall timber and banged his head into some broken bottles and was knocked out and cut some, and when he came to in a minute or so Joey was trying to wipe away the blood off his head. Somehow that made him like crazy, and he jumped up and beat Joey and knocked him down and tromped him till he was tired. Then he went home. When they found Joey they thought he was dead and for months in the hospital they thought he was not going to make it. But he made it kind of.

He had something wrong with his spleen and his central nervous system that made him walk a little funny and in his head where the skull fracture had squeezed his brains. Also a broken rib done something to his heart. And according to the state law, a death resulting from an assault was murder even if it happened a long time after. With all that, any punch or fall was liable to take Joey right off. Dwight knew that and Joey knew that. If ever they found Joey dead the chances were that whatever killed him would not of killed him without he was so messed up, and any coroner would be able to tell. So all Dwight could do was try to see to it that Joey did not get into trouble.

"Every once in a while he gets to brooding about he will never get married or go to college or be like other people, and he goes out and drinks and tries to get himself clobbered so maybe I will wind up in the chair, and also he likes to see me doing all I have to do to take care of him." He looked down at Joey for a long time and then up at me. "He moved from home to Philadelphia and then to Macon and Cleveland, Ohio and now here, and I had to go along too." He looked down at Joey again and said, "I never went to college either and I never got to marry anybody or have kids, I guess I never will. It's twenty-two years now."

I said, "Well, you have just made me feel one hell of a lot better." I said, "I been looking all my life for somebody who does things for other people without he gets anything for it and if I ever found one I believe it would blow my mind." I said, "All the dogs eating all the dogs, I can understand that and I can see how the whole thing works, but if ever you show me one guy who will do big things for other people just because they need doing, I will freak out." And I said, "What the hell are you laughing at?"

He said, "You're one."

I said, "No I ain't." I ran away saying No I ain't. I don't want to be like that, I don't want anyone to be like that, if anyone was like that, I wouldn't understand how things work.

Crate

We had to bury the pilot and Mr. Petrilli and the Stein kid,
and by the time we were done with that we had to bury
Rodney. It was a hell of a job for a bunch of kids but Miss
Morin made us. The pilot had no face and not much head and
Mr. Petrilli's chest was all squashed and the Stein kid didn't
seem to have a mark on him, I guess he died of scare before
the boat hit. Rodney screamed until Miss Morin gave him
that stuff. After that he just lay there until he died. Also Miss
Morin was hurt but nobody knew it at the time. She was up
and around before anybody, after the crash, telling everybody what to do. She was always a great one for that. You
want to be a probation officer, you be like that. Miss Morin,
she was a probation officer before she was born, I bet when
she was born she had that same set of lines around her mouth
old maids get from sucking their own mouth instead of
someone else's.

After we planted the people we wanted to take it easy but
she told off Fatty and Pam to drag out some food and set it
up while Tommy and Hal and Flip had to get into the hold
and bring out a crate. There was a lot of crates in there and
most of them was triangles, full of panels for building dome
houses, but it wasn't just any crate she wanted, it was one
special one. She give Tommy a paper with the special
numbers wrote on it big, and they had to slide half a hundred

115

crates in and out to look before they found the right one. They got it out and it was hard, with the ship tipped over that way and Flip getting under foot all the time. He was nine. Tom was fifteen, big. Hal was fourteen but not much bigger than Flip. The crate weighed about a hundred pounds.

We sat on the ground outside and ate except Miss Morin. She sat on the crate. That's the way she was, she always stood or sat a little higher than everyone else, one of her tricks. She was full of tricks. She was the most iron-handed hardmouthed cold-blooded old bitch ever lived. She was always around. She told us what to do and she was around to see it got done. There was other probation officers back on Earth had groups like us, overflow kids that didn't fit in nowhere and got into trouble and they shipped them off to frontier planets where they could fight cold and heat and animals instead of other people and the "Great As Is" (well that was what they said they was doing, we always thought they was just finding some edge to dump us off); anyway, other probation officers made up stuff for their kids to do and then went off on their own and when they came back, if it wasn't done they would put one or another of the kids in Detention or all of them. Miss Morin never did that, she was always around, she never went off on her own business, she had no business but us. She didn't use Detention, she didn't need it, she was a walking Detention all by herself. Also the other Probation Officers rode herd on a group until they was shipped out and then got theirselves another bunch. Not Miss Morin. When the day came for us to go, there she was, she'd fixed it to come along too. Nobody knew for sure what it would be like Outside, the only thing to look forward to was being away from your PO, and look at this, we had our PO right along with us.

So while we ate she made this speech. She said what we already knew, that there wasn't no place for kids like us on Earth, we'd all had our chance to shape up and we didn't, we were lucky to live in a time when there was frontier worlds where there could be a place for us, because in earlier times there wasn't no place and we would of been calmed down by wiping out part of our brain and be fit to push a mop for life, and in a earlier time still we would of spent most of our time in like Detention but much worse, with bars on the windows. But now there was the Jump Drive and a way of space-bending, like if you put two dots on a paper a long way apart and then bend the paper so the dots are together, you could jump from one to the other without hardly moving, and in no time. So with the Jump Drive there was ships going to thirty or more brand-new worlds and more found all the time, with plenty of room for overflow people and plenty of work and room for the likes of us that was so much trouble. This here was one of the new worlds, it was called Barrault and it was a dangerous place but it could be a good one if we got it tamed down. And we did not have to do it ourself, there was already a town called Cap Sidney.

Miss Morin went on to tell us more we already knew, like our boat crashed. Jump Drive ships don't land no place, boats off them do. So when they turned our boat loose it come into Real Space in the middle of a magnetic storm and nothing worked right. The pilot done the best he could but without radio or radar or ground control he couldn't do much. So he was dead and Mr. Petrilli and two of the kids, and that left Miss Morin and the five of us. The ship wouldn't know we crashed, you don't contact Jump Ships from Real Space because they ain't in it. Also they wouldn't know we'd crashed at Cap Sidney neither, they had no way of knowing when a boat would come unless they got told by the boat, which we didn't do without no radio because of that storm.

So now Miss Morin come to the point which was what we had to do next. We had to eat all we could and sleep a lot and then in the morning start out for Cap Sidney. There would not be nobody looking for us and there was no sense hanging around by the wreck, it did not carry no more food and water than it needed for a few orbits, and more than half of that was lost in the crash.

She told us how to get to Cap Sidney. Go straight east—that

meant walk into the sun all morning and keep the sun behind us all afternoon. Then we would come to a river, and we had to follow it downstream till we come to Cap Sidney. She made it sound real easy and I don't know if any of us listened real hard.

But then she come to the part about the crate, and we listened to that all right, because she got off it and kneeled down on the ground and made her voice kind of whispery and talked about that crate as if it was full of the greatest treasure in all the world, any world. She said, "Back on Earth not one of you had a chance of growing up to be anything or have anything. Out here you have. Now, you weren't to know this, but because of the crash, I'll tell you. This crate is the greatest treasure known to man, but it has to be taken to the Preceptor at Cap Sidney before you can get your share. Don't open it—you would not understand what is in it if you did. And I want you to understand what I'm saying—this treasure is not for me or for the colony, it's for you. It's yours and nobody will cheat you out of it and nobody can take it away from you. But you have to get it to the Preceptor."

I guess it was about this time we began to realize that Miss Morin wasn't planning to go along with us. Nobody liked the old razorback but the idea of getting away from her was a little bit spooky. We just weren't used to it. We all got real quiet. Then she started to cough. She used to cough once in a while like that. She didn't make almost no noise at all because she held a big handkerchief up tight against her nose and mouth, but it was like she was being hit by big fists the way it shook her. We just sat and waited it out like we always did. It lasted longer than usual and for a time she kneeled there with her head on the crate and the cloth up against her mouth. Nobody made a move to touch her. You did not touch Miss Morin. When she got up she stood up straight as ever. Pam saw something she did not tell about until later. Nobody else saw it.

Then Miss Morin gave orders about getting the crate ready

to carry, fixing a handle on each corner and screwing in eyebolts around the edge so we could lash our food and water on the top. Then she told Pam to come with her and went and climbed back into the busted tipped-over ship. The rest of us went on working on the crate. After a time Pam came back looking real quiet and stiff and said for Flip to go see her. Flip come back after a while and he looked scared. He said for Fatty to go in. Well, one at a time we went in to see Miss Morin, all five of us. She had something special to say to each one of us and said it was private, so let's keep it that way for now. We turned in soon as it was dark, sleeping outdoors near the crate. In the morning Miss Morin was dead. We could see her in there through the glass port in the door, but the door was locked from the inside. Her eyes was open and she'd throwed up a lot of blood. I bet she tried hard not to do that but she did anyway. Maybe we would have buried her too but like I said, she locked herself in and there wasn't nothing to do but get going. Tommy was the biggest, he was fifteen, and when he said let's go, we went. Tommy and Hal and Fatty took the three handles and Pam and Flip walked along ahead. It wasn't too long before Fatty begun to whine about how heavy the crate was, and Pam took over. Fatty kept on whining but not so loud. Flip was all over the place, ahead, behind, all over; well, Flip was only nine. He told what Miss Morin had said to him private. It was "Always ask somebody first."

It did not get too hot that first day although the air was very dry. We could look back and see the boat for a long time. It was plains country covered mostly with a brown weed. We seen like a mouse with six legs and a whole bunch of bugs that run sideways like crabs and one time a bunch of big knob-headed birds like ostriches away off, watching us. After a time we couldn't see the boat no more, it just went out of sight in that rolling country, you'd think it sank. We had to yell at Fatty to take over from Pam. Pam would not complain but she got tired easier than the others. Pam was fourteen but not very big. We wanted to stop but Tommy made us keep dragging until the sun was right overhead and then we lay up until we could be sure which way it was setting, so we'd know which way to go. We ate some and drank a little of the water, Tommy wouldn't let us have but a little, and we lay around in the shade and talked a little, some about Miss Morin. A funny thing happened about that:

Somebody said something about what a ironbound bitch she was, she wouldn't give you a cup of water if you was drowning, if she had a kind word for anybody it would choke her, and the next thing you know Flip was screaming at us. Flip! Flip was a fuzzyheaded little nine-year-old, I guess some people would say he was kind of cute, but mostly he was underfoot and asking questions and running when it was easier to walk, make you tired just looking at him. Well you know how little kids are. Anyway here he was yelling at us that Miss Morin was not either a ironbound bitch, we was all a bunch of ironbound bitches and we stunk too. I mean he was mad and crying. After a time he was sad and crying, which is a lot different, and he told us that one time at the Probation Center he got up tight and tried to run away, he couldn't've been no more than seven. It was at night and nobody could get through the force-fences, but he didn't know that and he tried for a long time and then it got cold and he flopped down by one of the fence generators. And who should come along but Miss Morin, she must've been looking for him half the night, and she did not say nothing but sat down beside him, and he climbed up into her lap and went to sleep and she held him like that until morning and took him back and never gave him no Detention. We listened to him bug-eyed because we could not believe Miss Morin would do such a thing but we could not disbelieve Flip telling about it crying.

Soon as the shadows started pointing east we got ourselves together and started east too. Fatty got to whining worse than ever and we let Flip help on that corner. After the third time Flip stepped on Fatty's feet, Fatty was ready to kill him and chased him away and then couldn't whine so much.

It was getting more hilly and we come over the top of a rise and down in a little valley it looked like somebody had built something. I mean there was five or six things standing up out of the ground, like if you have a oval bowl and cut it in two crosswise and stand it up on the cut. A couple were two or three feet tall and the others as tall as a man and then there was one really big one, I mean twelve foot or more. Flip, he went bouncing down the slope to see what they were, he had no more sense than a puppy dog. As we worked our way down the hill we could see that in front of each of the half-oval things there was a patch of bare purplish rock, or it looked like rock, dished down with kind of a wet mud in it, and back at the bottom of the tall thing, half sunk in the slime, a thing almost as big as your head, red and green and a shivery sort of yellow. We thought at first it was some kind of animal trapped or tied in there, because when we came up closer it began to wobble and spin and wiggle and swell up and all. Also there was a very sweet sticky smell that came up. Flip I guess wanted a closer look at that ball-thing inside, and in he went to look at it close or poke at it. Soon as he touched it the whole tall half-oval, like on a hinge, slammed down like a big mouth closing. My God I could feel the ground shake. Fatty started to scream and scream. We dropped the crate and ran over there. The big oval thing lay flat down now, it was covered with brown bark and it was made of hard wood. Flip's hand and forearm stuck out from one side. Tommy hit Fatty to stop the screaming and tried to get his fingers in the crack and lift, and Hal grabbed Flip's wrist and tried to pull him out. Tommy couldn't budge the thing, and the hand and forearm up to the elbow came off, chomped right in two. Fatty started to scream again and Hal fell down on his back and dropped the arm and looked at it and throwed up.

However we all were at first, it turned into a big mad. We jumped and kicked at that big closed thing, laying there like a great big wooden clam. We couldn't barely dent it. Then somebody thought of the bag of firemakers we had with us, discs about as big as your hand, you pull out the string and it begins to burn. Hal pulled the string on one and throwed it into one of the other clam-things, and it came down *whomp!* shaking the ground, and after a time smoke come out all around the edge. So we killed them all with the firemakers. You'd've thought we was all crazy the way we laughed. You would have to be there, be us, before you could understand how it was we could laugh at all that. We built a fire on the big closed one that got Flip, but it kept going out. I don't think we really hurt that one none.

We buried the arm and said the same words we said over the pilot and Mr. Petrilli and the Stein kid and Rodney, and picked up the crate and moved on.

We got into foothills before dark and found a place against a wall of rock and built a fire and ate and drank some more of our water. We got out the sleeping bags, they didn't weigh but a few ounces each but once they was inflated they were snug. Pam got into hers and Tommy went to get in with her, and before you know it Hal caught him by the shoulder and snatched him backwards and bowled him right over.

Tommy was big and broad and had shiny teeth, and Hal couldn't never have knocked him down if he expected it but he didn't. It could be Hal was even more surprised than Tommy because he did not try to stomp him or anything. Tommy rolled right on over and come up on his feet and dived on Hal and they went round and round. Hal got in a couple of real good ones because he was so mad but it wasn't no contest. Tommy beat the hell out of him and stood back and let him get up, and when Hal went for him again he beat the hell out of him again. So Hal quit. Tommy went back to Pam.

Pam said no, get away, and called to Hal. She said "Hal, you're going to sleep with me." Tommy let out a roar at that and wanted to know why, and Pam told him straight. She said, "Miss Morin said if anybody got to fighting over me I was to sleep with the loser. Now you both think about that the next time you want to fight." And she held open the sleeping bag until Hal got through the thing of not believing his ears and the thing of creeping past Tommy trying to be sure he wouldn't hit him again anyway and at last got in. Tommy just stood there shaking his head and after Hal was in with Pam he went and got his own bag and got in it and turned his face to the rock wall.

Much later in the night when the fire had burned down real low and it was quiet, Tommy woke up. Pam was slipping into his sleeping bag. She whispered, "Well, she didn't say I couldn't sleep with the winner too." But would you believe, Tommy kicked her out.

The next day was the thirsty day, and it was *this* close to being the last day alive for Fatty. The way Tommy and Hal looked at each other from time to time you would think there was going to be a murder. Also Tommy was plenty mad at Pam and Pam was still stung at getting kicked out like that, I mean, no woman likes to get turned down like that. In the middle of all this there's Fatty, whose feet hurt, who is thirsty, who wants to know how much longer this trip is going to take, and most of all, over and over and over again, "Why do we have to carry this thing?"

It got so that the big reason for carrying the crate was to bug Fatty. That whine was enough, after a while, to make the rest of us join forces and forget what we had going against each other.

We climbed. I don't know what we would of done if it was overcast. We were going west, but as the mountain grew steeper and rougher we had to go north for miles, sometimes, and then cut back again to go around. Once we spent three hours lowering ourselves into a canyon that seemed to turn west and climb again to a pass high to the south, only to find it was a dead end after a turn at the bottom, and it took us seven hours to haul ourselves and the crate back out again, right back to where we had started. We camped there too, and there wasn't but a splash of water left. Aside from being mad, Pam and Fatty were holding out pretty well, and of course Tommy was a bull, but Hal wasn't making it. He didn't say anything, but the way he slumped down when we stopped to rest, and the way he kept on panting for breath long after the rest of us were cooled down and ready to go, it worried us. Really the reason we camped where we did was that Hal passed out. I mean he just buckled at the knees and went down. Pam saw his head bump, bounce a little on the rock. She dropped her corner of the crate and went to him and sat him up, leaning against her, and wiped his face with her sleeve. He wouldn't open his eyes and when she opened one for him you couldn't see anything but the white. Without saying anything Tommy came around with the canteen and measured out a share of water and fed it to him. It brought him around, and then right away he fell into a normal sleep, and we had to wake him up to eat.

That was the cold night. We fused three bags and all slept together or we couldn't've made it. Never be thirsty and cold at the same time. That is not good.

In the morning, first thing, Tommy gave Hal another drink, and three hours later, when we were near the peak, he gave him more. It was Fatty who realized what was going on. Maybe Fatty was looking for something more to whine about, I don't know. By now Pam was mostly handling the point and Fatty was full time on the left corner. Tommy held the right-side handle of the crate with one hand and kept his other arm around Hal, who could only stumble along glassy-eyed. Fatty quit complaining and took to watching Tommy all the time.

We reached the high pass, and down there, way down, we saw the river. Funny, how the sight of it made the little swallow of water that Tommy doled out seem like so much less. But we all of us knew that it wasn't the time to gulp it down. Fatty and Pam and Hal each got their share, and we went on, and not once until after the rain did Fatty whine.

And oh it rained, it came up like artillery, with no more warning than ten minutes of mugginess. Next thing you know we were bracing ourselves against the rocks and hanging on to the crate with hands, feet and teeth. The torrents of water roared and sprayed all around us, first out of the sky lashed by solid slamming fists of wind, and then from uphill as the water found its way around the crags and down the fissures, smashing into boulders and throwing spray high in the air. Just as quickly, the wet shrapnel from the sky quit, but the water on the mountain went on and on, hissing and roaring and shining in the sun. And as soon as he dared take his hands off the crate, there was Tommy with the canteen, catching a little waterspout with it, holding it steady until it *glugged* full and spit out and overflowed. Then he very carefully screwed on the cap, and turned to the spout off the rock, still running.

Fatty scrambled over to him and put a hand on his shoulder. "Take it very easy at first, Tommy." And winked.

Tommy said, "You don't miss a thing, do you, Fatty?" He got a mouthful of water from the rock and swished it around and spit it out before he sipped a little. Pam wanted to know what the talk was about. Hal came around the rock dripping all over and looking better than he had in two days. Tommy said to shut up. Fatty grinned and said no. "You know what he's been doing? Giving his own water ration to Hal." Tommy said again to shut up. Hal said, "Jesus, Tommy." Pam looked at Tommy like . . . like the way guys wish girls would look.

Tommy sounded a little sore when he said, "It wasn't me, damn yez all. Miss Morin, she told me to." He let that soak in. "She must've known what would happen. Or maybe she just knew . . . me. She said, if you come to hate somebody, do him a favor. A big one. That's why I gave Hal the water." He looked at Hal, and said, kind of surprised, "I don't hate you no more. How about that."

I think we could of said the thing about Miss Morin, how it really was with her, right then, except for what happened. Maybe even that's what Pam was going to say, because she jumped up and kind of, you know, capered, like it was more than she could hold, and said, "Listen, Miss Morin was—" and then she was gone, just—gone, because, what with that bash of rain and all, the mountain was different, there was an edge that was closer, and I guess slippery too. All three of us were side by side on our bellies yelling something I can't even spell, and looking down at Pam falling away, getting smaller and smaller, and hitting a cliff face and bouncing far out and down and smaller still and landing on a saddleback and sliding, and then there wasn't any Pam any more. Rocks and some mud, and then more rocks and a crazy gout of dry dust, uncovered by the rockfall, shot out of the cliff and went down after her, smoky and pretty in the new washed sunlight.

From belly-down, Hal bounced up on all fours, maybe ready to go after Pam. Not to get her, not to save her, just to be where she was. He was immediately surrounded by Fatty, arms, legs, hands, feet. Tommy was a little slower but much more effective. He pulled them both back from the edge. He was crying. Fatty was crying too, but what else? Tommy crying the way he did, it was awful.

We got the crate into Cap Sidney. I don't know how. I do know how. It was Fatty. Well, it was really Miss Morin. Here's what I mean. That Miss Morin, she knew us all, and what she cared the most about was that whatever was weakest in each of us would have a prop under it when the load got big. The only one it didn't work on was Flip, well hell, little kids, they forget. Hal told us what her private word was to him. She told him "Hold out for the biggest reward—the one you'll live with." Fatty explained that to him all the way. Fatty told him going after Pam, now or later, wasn't anything he could live with. He didn't know what he wanted to live with after Pam went, but Miss Morin said to live with something—to *live*.

It was Fatty, too, who said to Tommy that Miss Morin wanted that crate to get to Cap Sidney. He only had to be told that once.

It worked, and seeing it work made it all come crashing through to Fatty. What Miss Morin had said to Fatty was,

"When it all comes apart, you put it together." Seeing it work changed Fatty from a kid to a girl. She was only twelve. Later on it would change her to a woman.

It took eight days to get down the mountain and across the river and to Cap Sidney, and it took eight hours for the Preceptor to convince us that what was in the crate was nothing—nothing but triangular insulating boards for a geodesic dome, and they had plenty of them already and could get the rest from the boat now they knew it was there. We were pretty mad at first. It almost came all apart again, we were so mad. And then Fatty put it together again for us. She said the one thing that made all the difference to us, because you got to remember who we were, the overflow, the can't-fit, the unwanted.

She said, "How many times would we have fell apart without that crate to carry? How far would we have got without we stuck by it and taken care of each other? The treasure she promised us if we got it through was just what she said it was—the greatest treasure known to man—to be alive. The treasure wasn't in the box, it was bringin' the box." Then she said it, Fatty did, she said what made the big difference to all of us forever and ever afterward; she said: "That Miss Morin, she loved us. She really and truly loved us."

The Girl Who Knew What
They Meant

I came out of the motel office feeling—well, feeling whatever it is you feel when you've just gotten a phone call from
somebody saying "You've got a week, Sam," and who will
call once more: "You've got one more day, Sam," and then
you're dead. I guess the only thing in the world that could
have shifted my mind away from it even for a second would
be a girl.

This one did, only for a second or maybe three. It was the
dog first, I guess. Afghan. Always did like Afghans. Have a
friend back East who knows this, once sent me a whole book
on Afghans—history, care and feeding, show points, pictures
of past champions. This one was a honey-colored bitch all
long bones and silk, and that's about all I took in just then
because of the girl. She had the dog on a plaited leash. She
was dressed in baggy old levis and an oversized man's white
shirt with the tails out, which is a way Miss Universe could
dress in a men's prison and not be noticed. But the sun was
on her face and hair and her hair was just the color and even
more silky than the Afghan's. Also her eyes were very wide
apart and matched her hair and the dog and the sunlight, and
she wasn't wearing a brassiere, which isn't easy to notice
under such circumstances but I can. I have a glandular
condition that makes me notice those things.

The whole thing stopped me in my tracks and I met her

eyes, and I said (now you've got to believe me—of all the things in the whole wide world I might have said, I had to come out with this one) I said: "It's a beautiful day."

And she said, "Why, thank you." And smiled.

Then my two or three seconds were up and reality came crashing all around me with one more week, and one more phone call and bang you're dead, and I went back to my room to sweat it out.

But you can't stay feeling any particular way permanently, leastways not at the peak (like scared at that type of phone call) except maybe mad, and in a few hours the fear had gone back to the sprained-ankle kind of dull throb. It's not filling the world any more, and it's with you every step of the way, but at least you can think of other things too.

And what I got to thinking of was this girl, and it wasn't only the way she looked. I got to playing back that conversation in my head. *"It's a beautiful day."*

"Why, thank you."

Now is that what they call in TV courtroom scenes "a responsive answer"?

Not if you look at the words. If you look at the words they don't make any sense at all. But you don't look at the words. You look at why I wanted to make contact, and what made me say what I said, of all stupid things, and how she answered that instead of the words. She knew just exactly what I meant.

I had a rush of brains to the head and got to rummaging around in the back of the closet where I'd thrown magazines and old Sunday papers, and there it was, the book. I got it out and banged the dust off it and went down to the office of the motel. It was a real cheap motel, twenty-one rooms and only one telephone which was fine on both counts. You can hide a lot if you live in a place like that. I found Mrs. Walker who came out of her apartment looking worried. She was the manager and how she looked didn't mean anything, she just had one of those worried faces.

I said, "Where's the chick with the dog?"

She said, "Now, Sam."

Is that responsive? I said, "Come on."

She said, "Number Five, but she's a nice girl, Sam." I guess if you look exactly at the words people use, it can get pretty weird. I mean they don't say what they're saying much at all, do they?

I crossed the court to Number 5 and rapped. After a bit the door opened a little bit. The white shirt was buttoned with three buttons only and she went to work on the fourth one as soon as her hand was off the doorknob.

"Here's a book you want to borrow from me."

"Book?" She looked at it as I held it up, and smiled. I didn't try to tell you what that smile was like the first time. I won't try about the second time either. She knew that book. "Oh, I always wanted a copy, but it's too expensive."

"Well you can take your time with it. Soon as I saw your dog I knew you'd want to have a look at it so I dug it out."

"I really appreciate it." That smile.

"It's all right." I backed off a step and made the Oke sign with my free hand. "See you around." I started to walk off and heard the door close softly behind me. You don't push at first. Later you push.

Then I turned around and knocked again. She opened and said, "You forgot to take the book."

She didn't laugh. "You forgot to give it to me." Then she opened the door all the way and made Come In with her hand.

I went in and put the book down on the dresser. It was a room like all the other rooms in the place—small, a double bed, plastic curtains with dust on them, walls with smog on them, suitcase-sized refrigerator with two electric burners bolted into the top and you could wash your dishes in the bathroom sink. For four bucks a night or ninety a month with linens and utilities, who cares? She had a piece of green glass, the kind they break out of a mold, big as my two fists, standing on the night table and some books, not the kind I ever read, and of course the dog. I scratched the dog in that hollow place under and behind the ear and she liked it.

I sat down on the one puffy grimy chair and she sat on the bed with one ankle under her. We talked about her working at the veterinarian's two blocks away and she couldn't get any place to live cheap enough with a dog. Animals. California, especially Southern California, LA is not like any other city in the world with a feeling to it, like a San Francisco feeling, a Chicago feeling, New York, New Orleans, they all have a special thing you would know in fifteen seconds with your eyes closed, but there is no such thing as a Los Angeles feeling. When you get to know it well you find there is a Pasadena kind of feeling that is not the same as Beverly Hills, and Encino sort of tastes different from Pacoima or Glendale, but there is no such thing as a real city-wide city flavor in LA. And I have a theory that no matter how long people live in LA they have no roots. They mostly come from other places and they had no roots there either, they cut them before they came or they just never had any, so it's like the whole place is adrift. And she said, "What's the matter?"

I said, "Nothing." I'd been laughing a lot too.

She made coffee and I heard about the guy she was going to get married to only he got drafted and menengitis in boot camp and died, and how her folks made it so hard on her because they lived together before he went away and since then somehow her folks blamed her. "Not that they ever said that, but whatever they said, that's what they meant." Then we had dinner, she cooked it, she didn't have anything but eggs so we ate those, and somehow it was ten o'clock and we were talking about snapping turtles, how if you stand on them it doesn't hurt them but they pull in their necks and you can drill a hole in the edge of their shell to put a chain on and they never feel it, if you want to keep one for a pet, and all of a sudden she held out her arms and that was it.

She had the most beautiful body I have ever seen. She did not wear brassieres for three reasons. One was they made her feel bound up and she did not want to feel bound up in any way. The other two reasons, one was on the right and one on the left, big and firm and perfect and holding themselves up and out without help from anything. She didn't like to wear clothes at all, that was where it was at. I have seen that before, but always chicks who went for see-through clothes and low-cut this-and-thats, peepshow for everybody. With her it was a private personal thing. Once she said "When you're naked you can lie to another naked person but it's not easy." She was a tremendous lay and she did not know or use any tricks. She just was.

Well for three days she was at work or we were together every waking or sleeping minute. One night she woke me up and the whole room was like echoing. She said I was cussing in my sleep, shouting. She was afraid. She asked me what was the matter and I told her nothing. I tried to go to sleep again and she held me and I think I cried.

So I told her about Millikein, he had it figured I was responsible for what happened to his brother, he had his mind made up I had to die too. Millikein had more money than God, but I don't think that would have made any difference; he was a man who made his mind up and that was it. He made up his mind I was going to die on his kid brother's birthday and he told me a whole year ahead. I ran a lot and hid a lot but he always found me and called me up or wrote me a letter as soon as I stopped, or I would meet him on the street. He even bought a beer bar, called Bash West, up the street. He always talked real nice to me, and I could go see him any time I wanted to; the only thing was, I was going to get killed four days from now. If it was a blackmail thing or something about money that I could pay off, well fine, but it wasn't. And what I told her was there wasn't any use going to the cops because who would listen to a story like that? I just didn't mention that if I got the cops smelling into my business with Millikein's brother, it could get even worse.

Well the next afternoon I was laying on my bed which I had

swung around so I could see across the court toward Number 5, so I would know when she got home from work, and I saw this chick, and even with what was going down between me and the girl with the Afghan, the first look at what walked in to that motel court brought me bolt upright. I mean the skirt up to here and a see-through blouse with just a couple little pockets here and here, and the hair fixed just so, wow, and long legs and a front end the like of which I swear I had seen only once in my life, and that was in Number 5.

Well sure it was in Number 5. It wasn't till the chick took out her key that I realized it was the same girl. Just because she didn't like to wear clothes didn't mean she didn't have them or didn't know how to wear them.

I was over there so fast I don't know yet whether I went out my door or through it. She was in the bathroom in mesh panty-hose washing makeup off her face. Makeup. Her.

I said "Where have you been?" and she said with Millikein. She said she had to see him, she had to find out if it was all true.

I said she thought I was a liar and she gave me a look so—I think tired is the word, such a long tired look I felt something wring inside. She said it wasn't that, she said she had to talk to him to see if he meant it. She said when people talked to her she knew what they meant. By this time I was willing to buy that, I'd seen it happen with her often enough. So I asked her what he said.

She dried her face and shook out her hair and came into the room. She took off the panty-hose and threw them in the corner. I never saw her do anything like that before. She fell down on the bed and told me he spoke real nice about me. He said he was just trying to throw a scare into me in case. He said he didn't have proof of nothing. He said really he thought I was a nice young guy, just irresponsible sometimes and not bad. He said to her not to say anything to me, really because of what had happened I ought to have a good scare thrown into me, don't spoil it because it was doing me a lot of good in the long run.

133

I kind of blew my top at her because she nosed into it and I called her some things that hurt, I guess, that whole long body twitched when I yelled them at her. And I said she'd have to pay off for mixing into it because now Millikein would have to get rid of her too, what would he figure if he wanted to wipe me out and here was a chick knew all about it? And I said even if he was changing his mind, she had made him change it right back again, running off at the mouth like that.

When I ran out of breath she rolled over and sat up and pushed the hair back from her face. I think I will always remember her like that no matter what else happens. So Goddam beautiful, not only a naked chick, that's great, but she had a way of being naked like it was clothes, if you see what I mean, good ones, she wore it well like something made for her and cut so well she could forget about it, knowing it was perfect. Oh damn words anyway, that's what this whole thing is about, damn words anyway.

So I came down off it and sat next to her and told her it was a hell of a way to take good news like that, I felt the first hope I had for a whole year or more, and I know she did it for me. So we went to bed.

The next day she didn't come home from work at all.

I waited for more than an hour and suddenly got filled up with the worst wild panic I ever had in my life. I ran up the street toward Bash West and from more than a block away I could see the blinking red lights and the people. Three police cars and two hogs and an ambulance. By the time I got there they were putting her in the wagon, I just got a flash of who it was, then the doors closed and it went howling off. They said somebody attacked a girl and she killed him defending herself. There was another meat wagon came then, and what they put in it had the blanket over its face.

Who can remember all that happened next the way it happened? Running and yelling, a whole lot of stuff about money, why should you need money at a time like that? Yelling at Mrs. Walker the manager to give me twenty so I could get a cab to the hospital, somehow, not that it makes any difference, knowing that when she gave in it was for me not for the girl in five, she wasn't a nice girl anymore because of me but me, I was still all right, what sense does that make? And then the cab that never came and when it came, standing still or running backwards all the way into Receiving Hospital, oh, forever, and then after all that running and yelling, waiting and waiting and waiting, looking at magazines I couldn't see, drinking coffee I couldn't taste out of the machine in the corridor.

Then the doctor, they must have raided a TV show for him, graying temples, tired eyes, stethoscope around his neck: Now she wants to see you very badly, only a few minutes, can't say which way it will go, really it all depends on her, she can pull through if she wants to.

And the corner of the IC Unit, that's Intensive Care in case you didn't know, all kinds of machines standing around, three nurses running between the beds, a burned kid, an old lady with both legs raised in the air with pulleys and breathing like a power hacksaw, and in the corner, there she was. The nurses put a screen around the bed and said Call me if, and Only a few minutes, and like that.

I thought she might be knocked out, but no, she was just waiting with her eyes closed. Eye. The other one was under the bandages that covered her whole head and half her face. Otherwise she was covered with a sheet.

She said to me, "Are you all right?" That's what she said.

I said, "I'm fine."

"He's dead." She closed her eye.

"That's what they tell me."

"Well then, you're all right now."

"Why did you do it?"

"He was going to kill you."

"That's not what you said."

"That's not what he said either." She could still smile a little. It wasn't the same, with the one eye. "But it's what he meant." Then she said for me to lift the sheet.

I didn't want to, but she said to. I did and said "Oh my God" and began to cry. She told me not to.

I said, "Listen, I don't care what it looks like, I am going to take care of you."

She said, "There's a whole piece cut right out of one of them. And I'm not going to get that eye back."

I said, "Oh, my God."

She looked at me for a long time with that one eye. It had that tired look. After a while she said, not mad or anything, "All my life I've known what people meant, no matter what they said, and I never met one yet that said what he meant. I don't think anyone knows how."

"That's crazy," I said. I told her I loved her. I told her I would always love her no matter what.

She looked at me for another long time, and then she said, "If I don't make it, will you take care of my dog? She's so beautiful, and she needs someone who will really take care of her."

I said of course she was going to make it.

"But in case," she said.

"I swear it."

She closed the eye. The nurse shoved the drape aside and looked in and told me to go.

She didn't make it, for some reason. Couple of days later I sold the dog and got out of town. I mean, LA really has no character.

Jorry's Gap

"Jorry!"

Dam*damn!* Jorry never said dam*damn* out loud; it was something that happened inside his head when he realized he couldn't get away with whatever, or when it wasn't going the way he wanted it to. "Yeh Mom." How come she could hear him even when Pop had his head in the boob-tube with horses galloping and gunshots and all, every time?

Mom got up and stood in the door of the living room and looked at him as he stood at the bottom of the stairs where he had just stepped over the third step which squeaked and timed it with the big noise on the TV and all. She said, "You're going out."

"Well yeh."

"You're not going out."

"It's early."

"Out till all hours, and where, and who with, I want to know."

"It's Friday."

"Speak to your son."

Without moving his eyes from the tube, Pop said, "What." Not a question, not an answer, just a flat statement "What."

Mom said to Jorry, "You're not going out."

Up to now it was like wired-in with relays, the way a traffic light does no matter what, red to yellow, yellow to green, green to red again. If he wanted to he could make the whole

137

thing go again: It's early, out till all hours and where and who with, it's Friday, speak to your son, what. So he tried the don't-worry.

"Don't worry, Mom. I'll be back early."

"Early in the morning early, five o'clock in the morning," Mom said. "With that addict Chatz."

"Chazz," he corrected. Chazz had a whole new thing with special words: lid, joint, roach, weed, grass. "You smoke?" meant something brand new. Chazz lied a lot and Jorry had never seen him with anything, and if he acted funny once or twice well, hell, you didn't need to blow a joint to learn that, you could learn it in the movies. Then yesterday Chazz said "I got a stash. You want?" and maybe it was a lie, but it scared Jorry like hell; he was real cool though: "Later, man." Now he said to his mother, "Nothing the matter with Chazz."

"With those eyes close together, round-shouldered," Mom said. "I can tell. Whatever he's taking now, even if he isn't he will and it will lead to something worse. Or it's that Jane."

"Joan." Dam*damn*. The instant he corrected her he knew she knew he had been thinking about pale parted hair and bright knowing laughter with some other guy, but with him a kind of *Finish your sentence, I got to go* even when all he said was hello. "That one," said Mom, "will give you a disease. Speak to your son."

"Wha-at. Wha-at." Pop still didn't take his eyes off the cowboys, but each "what" now had two syllables, and that meant he'd go into action if she gigged him once more.

"You'll hang around that Stube."

"Strobe," he corrected her before he could stop himself. "They don't have anything there, not even beer, only sodas and fruit juice."

"You're going to get killed riding around in that cheap flashy junkheap"—which was a hightailed Mustang with Shelby spoilers, oh wow—"which no man in his right mind would give to a retarded draft dodger like that Highball"—

"Highboy," Jorry said faintly.

—"no matter how much money he has. Speak to your son."

Dam*damn*. Now everything depended on how it was with the cowboys. If Pop was locked in to this show, it would be short. If not, this could go on for hours and nobody was going no place.

"What." Back to one syllable, but he yelled it, and he bounced out of the fat chair with a two-handed bang and came out of the living room, wattle-jawed, clamp-lipped, squinch-eyed. "Well what."

Mom said, "He's going out."

Pop said, "He's going out?"

Mom said, "He's not going out."

Pop said, "So go out, go out, a man has a right to work all day and come home and see one show all the way through."

Good, good, the show was good, this would be short.

"Go, go," Mom yelled, "Go to your creepy friends, never mind here where you get taken care of, eat the best food for your health, I work my fingers to the bone. Go."

Jorry went, feeling funny like he always did when it went this way, getting his way, winning, but all the same like thrown in the street, nobody cared enough. There is no word for a feeling like that. He went quickly but did not bump the door closed because sometimes that would bring Pop out on the porch, to make him come back. Behind him he could hear Mom starting in on Pop: how can I be his mother and his father all at the same time, he hasn't got a father who cares enough to keep him in the house running around at all hours with those creepy kids, and Pop yelling "After! After!" meaning shut up while he sees his show.

Jorry got as far as Third without seeing anybody, and then from out of nowhere there was Specs, waiting for the light to change. Specs had real bad skin and shorter hair than anyone else but he was always around the action and knew everything. "Highboy got Libby," was his greeting. Libby was a very unreachable chick; you see them carrying the flag at high-school assemblies and president of the Student Council and the honor roll and like that, and clean and kind and pretty and square, man, forget it. But with four hundred horsepower and a tach on the dash, Highboy gets Libby, vooming along dark roads anyplace for anything he wants, and back on time. "What else?" he said, and knew Specs understood him perfectly. The light changed and they walked across. Jorry stopped.

"Strobe," said Specs, announcing and asking.

"Not now." Jorry wasn't sure why not now. Maybe it was not wanting to arrive at the place with Specs; you didn't go anywhere with Specs, you found him there. And maybe it was wanting to be alone on a dark street for a while, to think about Libby on real leather next to you and the tach pushing up towards six, towards seven, towards someplace way out of town where nobody would know, and lots of time there and back early. Spec said, "Later, man," and walked. Jorry stood next to a high hedge and did his thing about the Mustang.

Maybe it took a while and maybe not; there's no time in there, but what brought him back was *bang* on the sidewalk with a little plastic handbag that skittered lipstick and Tampax and a cracked compact and some change all out and around.

It was Joanie with the long pale hair falling away from the clean pink part. She didn't see him and she said, "I don't *care.*" Then she stood quite still for the longest time with her eyes closed. Jorry didn't want to say anything while her eyes were closed, but then under the streetlamp he saw they were not closed tight enough to keep tears in, and the streaks on her face were like cracks in a doll if you put a light inside. So he picked up the handbag and touched her with it and said her name. She gasped and banged at the bridge of her nose with the back of her hand and looked at him. After a while she said, "Jorry," and took the bag.

"I was just standing here," was all he could say, and bent to pick up the compact and the Tampax. He found a quarter and a dime and straightened up. She held out the handbag, open, and he dumped the stuff into it and dropped the compact again. "Are you all right?"

She started to laugh in a way he didn't like at all, but by the time he had dipped down and up for the compact he realized that she wasn't laughing at him. It wasn't even laughing. Whatever it was stopped abruptly and she did something no girl he had ever heard of had ever done; she took his hand and put it against her breast. Never in all his life had he felt anything so soft and alive and wonderful. She asked him in a soft, breathy voice, "Is there anything wrong with that?"

"Well, no," was all he could say.

She lifted her hand away from his; it was up to him whether or not he left it on her. He dropped it away. His hand could still feel her; he had the crazy thought that it always would. She said, very slowly, "I have been so damn lonesome."

He just shook his head a little. He hadn't seen her around for a while but he couldn't ever remember her looking lonesome. Not ever.

"Jorry—"

"What?"

She wet her lips. "You know where I live."

"Well, yes."

"Look, I've got something to do right now, but I'll be home about eleven. There's nobody there tonight. You come."

"Well, I don't—" His mouth was suddenly too dry to release another word.

"I mean," she said, "I just don't *care.*" He was hung on her eyes like a coat on a nail. "Please, Jorry. *Please.*"

"Well, all right," he said, and she held him for a moment and then turned away; he thought his knees were going to buckle. He watched her walking away, long legs, long back, long hair all flogged by the shadows of tree trunks as she walked. "Oh wow," he whispered.

After a while he walked slowly down Third, somehow aware as never before of the impact of heels on pavement, the press of toes, the smell of a lawn mowed that afternoon and a hint of cat pee and how sharp blue starspecks could pierce a small town's Friday skyglow. Then and there he didn't feel any more like I'll-have-to-ask-Mom Jorry, or they-won't-let-me Jorry, or Jorry who was always on the outside looking in, or the inside looking on. "Man," he said quietly to the nighttime, "you got to do your thing." He was quoting somebody or other but he meant it. Then he was in the light, and who should be coming out of the candy store but Chazz.

Chazz had long green eyes and an eagle's beak and no chin, and a funny way of coming up to you as if he was walking a little sidewise. Jorry called him. It seemed to make Chazz glad. "Hey man."

Jorry made a c'mon motion with his head and walked away from lights and people and let Chazz catch up with him. They moved along for a moment and Joanie's I don't *care!*" popped into Jorry's head. It made him grin a little and it made a pleasant cold vacuum appear in his solar plexus: fun-fear. He said, in a Chazz-sidewise kind of way, "About that stash."

Pleased astonishment. Chazz banged his hands together once and smiled all around as if at an invisible audience in the dark, to whom he said, "He's with it, he's with it." He hit Jorry. "I about had you wrote off as a brownshoes."

"Me." Jorry knew how to use a question word as a flat statement. He liked how it came out. "Where's this grass?"

Chazz released a sudden roar of laughter and shut it off. Full of glee, he looked all around and sidewised up close, and said in a half whisper, "Man, I been *looking* for you. I just didn't know till now it was you." He began walking purposefully, and Jorry strode along beside him, willing enough but a little puzzled. They got to the next streetlight and Chazz looked all around again. "Roll up your sleeve."

"What?"

"Roll it up. I want to see something."

Jorry started to think something and then didn't want to think it. He rolled up his sleeve. Chazz grasped the biceps with both hands and squeezed and held on. Jorry tugged a bit, but Chazz held on, a great eagerness showing on his face. "What the hell you doing?"

"Shut up a minute," said Chazz, and hung on. He was peering at the crook of Jorry's elbow. Suddenly he released the arm. "Beautiful. Oh man, but beautiful."

"Beautiful what."

"Like that vein, it's a piece of hose, man."

"Chazz, what the hell you talking about?"

"Like you're like me, man. Some cats, you can't find it with an X-ray, but you and me, we got the gates wide open."

Jorry tried out the words. "Chazz, if you're holding we'll smoke. If not we'll Injun rassle or just forget it."

Chazz again produced that cut-off blast of laughter that went on in silent glee. When he could he said, "Smoke! That shit can wait, man. I got us a trip, not a buzz. Like four, six hours at twenty thousand feet with the wind behind us." He came close and whispered, "I got . . . speed."

"Speed."

There was a long pause. Jorry had the painful realization that I'll-have-to-ask-Mom, They-won't-let-me Jorry was maybe standing on a higher step, but he was still around. On the other hand, to have missed being a brownshoes by so close a margin, only to fall right out of this fellowship and back into Squaresville—it was unthinkable. And besides—he was scared. Veins—Speed—God. His mouth was suddenly completely dry, which had the odd effect of reminding him of something. He worked up spit and swallowed hard before he could say, very carefully, "Oh hell man, six hours. I got a date at eleven. I'm going to need everything I got."

"You don't need the date."

"Oh, huh."

"Who is it?"

"A chick."

"You're putting me on."

"Honest to God. Any other time, Chazz, but not tonight."

Apparently he said this just right too, because Chazz sounded real sad when he said "Oh wow," and hopeless when he said "She got a friend?" and Jorry knew for a second (he forgot it later) why round shoulders and a big nose and no chin was looking to shoot speed. Chazz bit on his lip a while and then said nakedly, "Look, I'm going to wait for you. Like I got it and I checked it out and I know how, but man I don't figure to fly solo, not the first time."

Jorry said, "I dig." What Jorry dug most was how scared Chazz was. He didn't have to look at whether or not he was scared or how much; this could come first and it made him grateful. He hit Chazz and said, "So later," and could see Chazz was grateful too. Then the Mustang flew in *wawoom* to the curb, nosed down and squatted there.

Highboy: crisp hair the color of French vanilla, white shirt, white sweater, white strong teeth, and next to him oh Libby. Oh. Highboy said, "Hey, who wants to make it with us to Little Gate?" Little Gate was forty miles away.

Chazz said so it showed, "Jorry's hung up, he's making out." Jorry thought from what he could see that Highboy liked this and Libby didn't, but what could that matter, ever? Chazz was saying, "But you could drop me by the Strobe, right?"

Highboy waved at his door latch: permission, but Chazz could open it for himself, and said to Jorry, "Keep the beat, baby," which was so-long and also something to do with making out, and made him feel pretty good, but all the same dam*damn* there go the taillights. And the funny thing was, he had to go by the Strobe to get to Joanie's house anyway. You never know why you play it the way you do.

At night (it isn't even there in the daytime) the Strobe is a wide bright storefront on a row of dark ones; light is a lake in front, with lightning; cars whale through it, people shark and minnow through it, and away a bit, once in a while, the Highway Patrol hawks by seeing everything, looking for something. Specs was there, knowing it all, and as soon as he saw Jorry's face he said to it, "Making out." Two words: congratulations, you didn't think you could keep it from me, who is it, if you don't tell me I'll find out anyway, you are maybe becoming something to notice around here, I'm watching you. All of which Jorry acknowledged: "You know how it is." He saw the Mustang in the middle of the light-lake, tail-up in a sprinter's crouch in the shallows two feet away from the curb; Highboys needn't park straight. Chazz wasn't there.

Specs said, "Three guys got burned by the same chick. Their folks got together and went to the school."

Burned. Jorry couldn't grab that, unless— "Who?"

Specs said who, three guys he knew, two of them were in History with him. But that wasn't what he wanted to know. He wanted to know who the girl was. He didn't want to ask and he didn't have to; Specs said it was Joanie. Dam*damn*. At which point Highboy and Libby came out of the Strobe and crossed to the Mustang. Highboy opened her door for her and that shining car fielded her like a good catcher's mitt. Highboy legged around front and slid in, and the chrome pipes growl-howled. From the Strobe came a chick with sit-on-it shining black hair and hip huggers tight as a blister, white, cut so low in front that "They give away shaving cream when you buy those," Specs said in his ear, and Highboy made a gesture that Jorry would remember all his life it was so great, that would last longer in his head even than what else happened right after. Highboy blew her a kiss. Highboy blew her a kiss right in front of and all around Libby and made Libby smile at it. Highboy blew that chick a kiss while he snapped his clutch and the wide ovals screamed him away in a burning launch; he blew her a kiss turning evenly in his luscious-leather bucket; he blew and threw his kiss in a wide steady backhand that ended with him smiling and releasing the last of it through the big wide rear window, all the while scorching rubber and squashed tight, him and Libby, against the welcoming seatbacks. So great.

Also he misfigured his angles. At the end of the row of dark stores and across a small street was no curb or sidewalk but a bare bank, low at first and tipping up steep, and the engineer doesn't live who could design it more perfectly to lift up the right side of a car and flip it, not to spin and flip, but to take off and corkscrew. It wasn't more than seventy, seventy-five yards from the Strobe that the Mustang flew and flipped and hit upside down and against an elm tree and burned. The Highway Patrol always knows what to do and they were there, but knowing how isn't enough sometimes.

Jorry walked home through the dark streets, trying hard to wipe out what was behind him without opening up what was in front, trying to get by himself, not with Jorry-maybe-you're-worth-watching or with Mom-can-I Jorry, but with himself; and who the hell might that be?

About Chazz and mainlining, about Joanie and the burn, about getting killed in the Mustang, he could have known without leaving the house. Mom said it all, Mom batted one thousand. He could've known it all even if she hadn't said it—but she did say it.

Also she said she worked hard and saw to it he ate and got good clothes and had a place for himself. She said it funny and she said it so often you didn't hear it any more, but she did say it.

Pop also said he worked hard all day and when he came home he had a right. He said it to Mom and he said it to Jorry. Then Jorry would say whatever it was he always said, and nobody heard him either.

Jorry began to walk faster.

Because if there was a way to say something to Mom, and if she could say it to him and to Pop, so that they heard each other, they wouldn't need to stay mad or feel useless, not any of them. Like if somehow you can make people just *listen* to each other, not just listen to you. And you listen too. Everybody.

Jorry began to run because he really believed you could make someone else listen. He knew because he'd done it. He'd listened to every word Mom said about tonight, the only thing was he couldn't hear it until later when those things happened. And now he really believed you could make

somebody listen *now*. And would you believe it, after all that
had happened it was still only a quarter of twelve.

He went in the back way because no matter what else, Mom
always had for him a way in. He locked the door from inside
because when he was in Mom liked the rest of everything
shut out. This seemed to mean something as he climbed the
stairs. He heard their voices up there, hammer-and-tongs. He
smiled to himself because he knew something they didn't.

It was the same thing he had heard going away: why can't
you speak to your son. And: Coming home I got a right. But
it was the same thing drawn out ragged and harsh: Jorry
realized that they had been going around and around since he
left. Believing that people could listen, listen and hear, he
knocked on the door.

Pop, undershirt, galluses down, the last straw was under the
angry eaves of his eyes and burning; Mom, gray pigtails (only
at night, pigtails) and so worn, so worn altogether out by not
being heard.

"Pop, listen."

"I wash my hands," Mom cried. "Do what you want, the
waste. Go in the ashcan, live there with your Chatz and the
other garbage. I wash my hands."

"Mom, listen."

Pop probably didn't hit him all that hard but it was so
unexpected and he wasn't at all ready. Lying down on the
floor of the upstairs hall looking up, with Mom screaming, he
saw his father big. Huge. Like he hadn't since he was three
years old.

"I had this for the last time and never again, you going out
and her on my back, so out of my sight," Pop bellowed and
spit flew.

Jorry sat up and then knelt up. He said "Pop, listen," or
maybe he thought he said it. As he knelt there Pop went for
him again, this time not with a man's punch like the other
one, but with a push in the face to throw him back and
skidding, the kind of push where being hurt isn't any part of
it, but insult is. "Out of my sight!" Pop bawled, crack-voiced,

and Mom was in the doorway and he pushed her too, back on the bed, and slammed the door. Somewhere in there Jorry stopped believing in anything.

He went back in town and did his thing here, and did it again there, and at a quarter to five he and Chazz were busted for use and holding, and a couple of weeks later the first chancre showed; that was in the House of Correction.

And that's how Jorry got started.

It Was Nothing—Really!

Having reached that stage in his career when he could have a personal private washroom in his office, Henry Mellow came out of it and said into the little black box on his desk "Bring your book, please." Miss Prince acknowledged and entered and said "Eeek."

" 'Ever since the dawn of history,' " Henry Mellow dictated, " 'mankind has found himself face to face with basic truths that—' "

"I am face to face," said Miss Mellow, "with your pants are down, Mr. Mellow, and you are waving a long piece of toilet paper."

"Ah yes, I'm coming to that. '. . . with basic truths that he cannot see, or does not recognize, or does not understand.' Are you getting this, Miss Prince?"

"I am getting very upset, Mr. Mellow. Please pull up your pants."

Mr. Mellow looked at her for a long moment while he put his thoughts on "hold" and tuned them out, and tuned her in, and at last looked down. "Archimedes," he said, and put his piece of toilet paper down on the desk. Pulling up his pants, he said, "At least I think it was Archimedes. He was taking a bath and when he lay back in it, displacing the water and watching it slop over the sides of the tub, the solution to a problem came to him, about how to determine how much base metal was mixed in with the king's gold ornaments. He jumped out of the bath and ran naked through the streets shouting *Eureka,* which means in Greek, 'I have found it.' You, Miss Prince, are witnessing such a moment. Or was it Aristotle?"

"It was disgraceful is what it was," said Miss Prince, "and no matter how long I work here you make me wonder. Toilet paper."

"Some of the most profound thinking in human history has come about in toilets," said Henry Mellow. "The Protestant reformation was begun in a toilet, when Luther was sitting there working on his—am I offending you, Miss Prince?"

"I don't know. I guess it depends on what comes next," said Miss Prince, lowering her hands from her ears, but not much. Warily she watched as he arranged his pennant of toilet paper on the desk and began tearing it, placing his hands palm down on the desk and drawing them apart. "You will observe—Miss Prince, are you getting this?"

She picked up her notebook from where she had flung it to cover her ears. "No, sir, not really."

"Then I shall begin again," said Henry Mellow, and began to dictate the memo which was to strike terror into the hearts and souls of the military-industrial complex. Oh yes, they have hearts and souls. It's just that they never used them until Henry Mellow. Notice the structure there. Henry Mellow was more than a man, he was a historical event. You don't have to say "Wilbur and Orville Wright and their first successful experiment at," you just have to say "Kitty Hawk." You can say "Since Hiroshima" or "Dallas" or "Pasteur" or "Darwin" and people know what you are talking about. So it is that things haven't been the same with the military-industrial complex since Henry Mellow.

The Mellow memo reached the Pentagon by the usual channels, which is to say that a Bureau man, routinely going through the segregated trash from the Mellow offices, found three pages done by a new typist and discarded because of forty-three typographical errors, and was assigned, after they had gone through all the layers of the Bureau to the desk of the Chief himself, to burglarize the Mellow offices and secure photographs of a file copy. He was arrested twice and injured once in the accomplishment of this mission, which was not reported in for some time due to an unavoidable accident: he left the papers in a taxicab after stealing them and it took him three weeks to locate the taxi driver and burglarize *him*. Meanwhile the memo had been submitted to the *Times* in the form of a letter, which in turn formed the basis for an editorial; but as usual, appearance of such material in the public media escaped the notice of public and Pentagon alike.

The impact of the memo on the Pentagon, and most especially on its target point, the offices of Major General Fortney Superpate, was that of an earthquake seasoned with a Dear John letter. His reactions were immediate and in the best military tradition, putting his whole section on Condition Red and invoking Top Secret, so that the emergency would be heard by no one outside his department. What then followed was total stasis for two hours and forty minutes, because of his instant decision to check out Mellow's results. This required toilet paper, and though General Superpate, like Henry Mellow, had a washroom at the corner of his office, he had enough respect for tradition to stifle his impulse to get up and get some, but instead summoned his adjutant, who snapped a smart salute and received the order. From the outer office the adjutant required the immediate attendance in person of the supply sergeant (remember, this was now a classified matter) who was on leave; the qualifications of his corporal had then to be gone into before he could substitute. Requisition papers were made out, with an error in the fourth copy (of six) which had to be adjusted before the roll of toilet paper, double-locked in a black locked equipment case, was delivered to the general. At this point he was interrupted by a Jamestown gentleman named (he said)

Mr. Brown: black suit, black tie, black shoes, and a black leather thing in his breast pocket which, when unfolded, displayed a heavy bright badge with eagles and things on it. "Oh damn," said the general, "how did you people find out about this?", which got him a smile—it was the only thing these Mr. Brown types ever really smiled at—while Mr. Brown scooped up the photocopy of the Mellow memo and the locked equipment case containing the roll of toilet paper. He left, whereupon the general, realizing with a soldier's practicality that the matter was now out of his hands, restored Condition Green and lifted Secrecy, and then felt free to step into his own washroom and do his own toilet-paper procurement. He returned with a yard or so of it, spread it out on his immaculate desk, placed his hands palms down on it and began to pull it apart. He turned pale.

The injection of the Mellow Memo into the industrial area is more of a mystery. Certainly it was the cause of Inland Corp's across-the-board six-percent reduction of raw material orders, and when a corporation as big, and as diversified, as Inland cuts back six percent, the whole market shakes like a load of jello in a truck with square wheels. This is the real reason for Outland Industries starting merger talks with Inland, because one of their spies had gotten the word to Outland, but not the memo, and the big wheels at Outland figured if they bought Inland, the memo would come along with the deal. Imagine their surprise, then, when the Chairman of the Board at Inland not only agreed enthusiastically to the merger, but sent along a copy of the memo for free. There is no record of the midnight meetings of the top brass of the two industrial giants, but when they broke up they were, it is reported, a badly frightened bunch. The dawn came up on many a wealthy suburb, estate, club and hotel suite to the soft worried sound of tearing toilet paper.

And paper towels.

And checks from checkbooks.

As for the merger, it was left in its current state of negotiation, neither withdrawn nor pursued, but waiting; meanwhile, Inland's order to reduce raw materials purchases was lowered to a compromised three percent while the world—the little, real world, not the mass, sleeping world—waited to see what would happen.

The Mellow Memo's most frightening impact, however, was on the secret headquarters in Jamestown. (It's probably the most secret headquarters in the world or anywhere else. No signs out front, unmarked cars, and everybody's named Brown. Sometimes twelve, fourteen lunches are delivered to the front office for "Mr. Brown." Nobody knows how they get sorted out. Everybody in town keeps the secret.)

They had done everything they could; Henry Mellow's home, office, person and immediate associates were staked out, tailed, and bugged, his probable movements computed and suitable responses by the Agency programmed, and there was nothing to do but sit around and wait for something to happen. On total assignment to the Mellow affair were three top agents, Red Brown and Joe Brown and a black-power infiltrator called Brown X. Due to the extremely sensitive nature of the Memo, Red Brown had sent Brown X off on an extremely wild goose chase, tracking down and interviewing Henry Mellow's ex-schoolteachers, kindergarten through fourth grade, in places like Enumclaw, Washington and Turtle Creek, Pennsylvania.

Red Brown rose from his pushbuttoned, signal-light-studded desk and crossed the room and closed the door against the permeating susurrus of computers and tapes and rubber footfalls and hand-shrouded phone calls: "Brown here. . . . Ready. Scramble Two. Brown out." Joe Brown watched him alertly, knowing that this meant they were going to discuss their assignment. He knew too that they would refer to Henry Mellow only as "Suspect." Not The suspect or Mr. Suspect: just Suspect.

Red Brown regained his saddle, or control tower—nobody would call it a chair—and said: "Review. Brainstorm."

Joe Brown started the tape recorder concealed in his black jacket and repeated "Review. Brainstorm," and the date and time.

"Just who is Suspect?" Red Brown demanded.

Comprehending perfectly that this would be a fast retake of everything pertinent that they knew about Henry Mellow, with an aim of getting new perspectives and insights, no matter how far out; and that he, Joe Brown, was on trial and on the record in a "have you done your homework" kind of way, Joe Brown responded swiftly, clearly, and in official *stacatto*: "WMA, five ten, unmarried, thirty-six years old, eyes hazel, weight one seventy—"

"All right, all right. Occupation."

"Writer, technical, also science fact articles and book reviews. Self-employed. Also inventor, holding patents number—"

"Never mind those or you'll be reeling off numbers all day, and besides you're bragging, Brown: I know that thing you have with numbers."

Joe Brown was crushed but knew better than to show it. Memorizing numbers was the one thing he did really well and patent numbers were where he could really shine. "Holds patents on kitchen appliances, chemical processes, hand tools, optical systems. . . ."

"Genius type, very dangerous. The Bureau's been segregating his garbage for eighteen months."

"What put them onto him?"

"Internal Revenue. Gets royalties from all over the world. Never fails to report any of it."

Joe Brown pursued his lips. "Has to be hiding something."

"Yes, not usual, not normal. Politics?"

"No politics. Registers and votes, but expresses no opinions."

Joe Brown pursued his lips again, the same purse as before, because it was part of the same words: "Has to be hiding something. And what happens if he turns this thing loose on the world?"

"Worse than the bomb, nerve gas, Dederick Plague, you name it."

"And what if he gets sole control?"

"King of the world."

"For maybe ten minutes." Joe Brown squinted through an imaginary telescopic sight and squeezed an invisible trigger.

"Not if he had the Agency."

Joe Brown looked at Red Brown for a long, comprehending moment. Before he had become an Agent, and even for a while when he was in training, he had been very clear in his mind who the Agency worked for. But as time went on that didn't seem to matter any more; agents worked for the Agency, and nobody in or out of the Agency or the Government or anywhere else would dream of asking who the Agency worked for. So if the Agency decided to work for the king of the world, well, why not? Only one man. It's very easy to take care of one man. The agency had long known how things should be, and with sole control of a thing like this the Agency could make them be that way. For everybody, everywhere.

Red Brown made a swift complex gesture which Joe Brown understood. They both took out their concealed recorders and wiped that last sentence from the tape. They put their recorders away again and looked at each other with new and shining eyes. If the two of them should come by sole possession of the Mellow Effect, then their superior, a Mr. Brown, and his superior, who was head of the whole Agency, had a surprise coming.

Red Brown removed a bunch of keys from his belt and selected one, with which he unlocked a compartment, or drawer, in his desk, or console, and withdrew a heavy steel box, like a safety deposit. Flicking a glance at his colleague to be sure he was out of visual range, he turned a combination knob with great care and attention, this way, that, around again and back, and then depressed a handle. The lid of the box rose, and from it he took two photocopies of the Mellow Memo. "We shall now," he said for the record, "read the Mellow Memo."

And so shall you.

THE MELLOW MEMO

Ever since the dawn of history, mankind has found himself face to face with basic truths that, through inattention, preconception, or sheer stupidity, he cannot see, or does not recognize, or does not understand. There have been times when he has done very well indeed with complex things—for example, the Mayan calendar stones and the navigation of the Polynesians—while blindly overlooking the fact that complex things are built of simple things, and that the simple things are, by their nature, all around us, waiting to be observed.

Mankind has been terribly tardy in his discovery of the obvious. Two clear illustrations should suffice:

You can, for a few pennies, at any toy store or fairgrounds, pick up a pinwheel. Now, I have not been able to discover just when this device was invented, where, or by whom, but as far as I know there are no really early examples of it. An even simpler device can be whittled by an eight-year-old from a piece of pine: a two-bladed propeller. Mounted on a shaft, or pin, it will spin freely in the wind. This would seem to be the kind of discovery which could have been made five hundred years ago, a thousand—even five thousand, when Egyptian artisans were turning out far more complex designs and devices. To put the propellor on a fixed shaft, to spin the shaft and create a wind, to immerse the thing in water and envision pumps and propulsion—these seem to be obvious, self-describing steps to take, and yet for thousands of years, nobody took them. Now imagine if you can—and you can't—what the history of civilization would be, where we would now be technologically, had there been propellors and pumps a thousand years ago—or three, or five! All for the lack of one whittling child, one curious primitive whose eye was caught by a twisted leaf spinning on a spiderweb.

It Was Nothing—Really!

One more example; and this time we will start with modern materials and look back. If you drill a one-sixteenth-inch hole in a sheet of tin, and place a drop of water on the hole, it will suspend itself there. Gravity will pull it downward, while surface tension will draw it upward into a dome shape. Viewed from the edge of the piece of tin, the drop of water is in the shape of a lens—and it is a lens. If you look down through it, with the eye close to the drop, at something held under it and well illuminated, you will find that the liquid lens has a focal length of about half an inch and a power of about fifty diameters. (And if by any chance you want a microscope for nothing, drill your hole in the center of the bottom of a soup can, then cut three sides of a square—right, left, top—in the side of the can and bend the tab thus formed inward to forty-five degrees, to let the light in and reflect it upwards. Cut a slip of glass and fix it so it rests inside the can and under the hole. Mount your subject—a fly's foot, a horsehair, whatever you like—on the glass, put a drop of water in the hole, and you will see your subject magnified fifty times. A drop of glycerin, by the way, is not quite as clear but works almost as well and does not evaporate.)

Microscopes and their self-evident siblings, telescopes, did not appear until the eighteenth century. Why not? Were there not countless thousands of shepherds who on countless dewy mornings were in the presence of early sunlight and drops of water captured on cobwebs or in punctured leaves; why did not just one of them look, just once, through a dewdrop at the whorls of his own thumb? And why, seemingly, did the marvelous artisans of glass in Tyre and Florence and ancient Babylon never think to look through their blown and molded bowls and vases instead of at them? Can you imagine what this world would be if the burning glass, the microscope, the eyeglasses, the telescope had been invented three thousand years earlier?

Perhaps by now you share with me a kind of awe at human blindness, human stupidity. Let me then add to that another species of blindness: the conviction that all such simple things have now been observed and used, and all their principles understood. This is far from so. There are in nature numberless observations yet to be made, and many of them might still be found by an illiterate shepherd; but in addition to these, our own technology has produced a whole new spectrum of phenomena, just waiting for that one observant eye, that one undeluded mind which sees things placed right in front of its nose—not once, not rarely, but over and over and over again, shouting to be discovered and developed.

There is one such phenomenon screaming at you today and every day from at least three places in your house—your bathroom, your kitchen, and, if you have a bank account, your pocket.

Two out of five times, on the average, when you tear off a sheet of toilet tissue, a paper towel, or a check from your checkbook, it will tear across the sheet and not along the perforated line. The same is true of note pads, postage stamps, carbon-and-second-sheet tablets, and virtually every other substance or device made to be torn along perforations.

To the writer's present knowledge, no exhaustive study has ever been made of this phenomenon. I here propose one.

We begin with the experimentally demonstrable fact that in a large percentage of cases, the paper will tear elsewhere than on the perforation line. In all such cases the conclusion is obvious: that the perforation line is stronger than the nonperforated parts.

Let us next consider what perforation is—that is to say, what is done when a substance is perforated. Purely and simply: material is removed.

Now if, in these special cases, the substance becomes stronger when a small part of it is removed, it would seem logical to assume that if still more were removed, the substance would be stronger still. And carried to its logical conclusion, it would seem reasonable to hypothesize that by removing more and more material, the resulting substance would become stronger and stronger until at last we would produce a substance composed of nothing at all—which would be indestructible!

If conventional thinking makes it difficult for you to grasp this simple sequence, or if, on grasping it, you find you cannot accept it, please permit me to remind you of the remark once uttered by a Corsican gentleman by the name of Napoleon Bonaparte: "To find out if something is impossible—try it." I have done just that, and results so far are most promising. Until I have completed more development work, I prefer not to go into my methods nor describe the materials tested—except to say that I am no longer working with paper. I am convinced, however, that the theory is sound and the end result will be achieved.

A final word—which surely is not needed, for like everything else about this process, each step dictates and describes the next—will briefly suggest the advantages of this new substance, which I shall conveniently call, with a capital letter, Nothing:

The original material, to be perforated, is not expensive and will always be in plentiful supply. Processing, although requiring a rather high degree of precision in the placement of the holes, is easily adaptable to automatic machinery which, once established, will require very little maintenance. And the most significant—one might almost say, pleasant— thing about this processing is that by its very nature (the removal of material) it allows for the retrieval of very nearly 100 percent of the original substance. This salvage may be refabricated into sheets which can then be processed, by repeated perforations, into more Nothing, so that the initial material may be used over and over again to produce unlimited quantities of Nothing.

Simple portable devices can be designed which will fabricate Nothing into sheets, rods, tubing, beams or machine parts of any degree of flexibility, elasticity, malleability, or rigidity. Once in its final form, Nothing is indestructible. Its permeability, conductivity, and chemical reactivity to acids

159

and bases all are zero. It can be made in thin sheets as a wrapping, so that perishables can be packed in Nothing, displayed most attractively on shelves made of Nothing. Whole buildings, homes, factories, schools can be built of it. Since, even in tight rolls, it weighs nothing, unlimited quantities of it can be shipped for virtually nothing, and it stows so efficiently that as yet I have not been able to devise a method of calculating how much of it could be put into a given volume—say a single truck or airplane, which could certainly carry enough Nothing to build, pave, and equip an entire city.

Since Nothing (if desired) is impermeable and indestructible, it would seem quite feasible to throw up temporary or permanent domes over houses, cities, or entire geographical areas. To shield aircraft, however, is another matter: getting an airflow through the invisible barrier of Nothing and over the wings of an airplane presents certain problems. On the other hand, orbiting devices would not be subject to these.

To sum up: the logical steps leading to the production of Nothing seem quite within the "state of the art," and the benefits accruing to humanity from it would seem to justify proceeding with it.

There was a certain amount of awe in Miss Prince's voice as it emerged from the little black box saying "A Mr. Brown is here and would like to see you."

Henry Mellow frowned a sort of "Oh, dear" kind of frown and then said, "Send him in."

He came in, black suit, black shoes, black tie, and in his eyes, nothing. Henry Mellow did not rise, but he was pleasant enough as he gestured, "Sit down, Mr. Brown." There was only one chair to sit in, and it was well placed, so Mr. Brown sat. He identified himself with something leathery that opened and shut like a snapping turtle with a mouthful of medals. "What can I do for you?"

"You're Henry Mellow." Mr. Brown didn't ask, he *told*.

"Yes."

"You wrote a memo about Noth— about some new substance to build things with."

"Oh that, yes. You mean Nothing."

"That depends," said Mr. Brown humorlessly. "You've gone ahead with research and development."

"I have?"

"That's what we'd like to know."

"We?"

Mr. Brown's hand dipped in and out of his black jacket and made the snapping turtle thing again.

"Oh," said Henry Mellow. "Well, suppose we just call it an intellectual exercise—an entertainment. We'll send it out to a magazine, say, as fiction."

"We can't allow that."

"Really not?"

"We live in a real world, Mr. Mellow, where things happen that maybe people like you don't understand. Now I don't know whether or not there's any merit in your idea or how far you've gone with it, but I'm here to advise you to stop it here and now."

"Oh? Why, Mr. Brown?"

"Do you know how many large corporations would be affected by such a thing—if there was such a thing? Construction, mining, hauling, prefabrication—everything. Not that we take it seriously, you understand, but we know something about you and we have to take it seriously anyway."

"Well, I appreciate the advice, but I think I'll send it out anyway."

"Then," continued Mr. Brown as if he had not spoken, and acquiring, suddenly, a pulpit resonance, "Then . . . there's the military."

"The military."

"Defense, Mr. Mellow. We can't allow just anybody to get their hands on plans to put impenetrable domes over cities—suppose somebody overseas got them built first?"

"Do you think if a lot of people read it in a magazine, someone overseas would do it first?"

161

"That's the way we have to think." He leaned closer. "Look, Mr. Mellow—have you thought maybe you've got a gold mine for yourself here? You don't want to turn it over to the whole world."

"Mr. Brown, I don't want a gold mine for myself. I don't much want any kind of mines for anybody. I don't want people cutting down more forests or digging more holes in the ground to take out what they can't put back, not when there are better ways. And I don't want to get paid for not using a better way if I find one. I just want people to be able to have what they want without raping a planet for it, and I want them to be able to protect themselves if they have to, and to get comfortable real quick and real cheap even if it means some fat cats have to get comfortable along with them. Not thin, Mr. Brown—just comfortable."

"I thought it was going to be something like this," said Mr. Brown. His hand dipped in and out of the black jacket again, but this time it was holding a very small object like a stretched-out toy pistol. "You can come along with me willingly or I'll have to use this."

"I guess you'd better use it, then," said Henry Mellow regretfully.

"It's nice," said Mr. Brown. "It won't even leave a mark."

"I'm sure it won't," said Henry Mellow as the little weapon went off with a short, explosive hiss. The little needle it threw disintegrated in midair.

Mr. Brown turned gray. He raised the weapon again. "Don't bother, Mr. Brown," said Henry Mellow. "There's a sheet of just plain Nothing between us, and it's impenetrable."

Still holding his weapon, Mr. Brown rose and backed away—and brought up sharply against some Nothing behind him. He turned and patted it wildly and then ran to the side, where he struck an invisible barrier that sat him down on the rug. He looked as if he was going to cry.

"Sit in the chair," said Henry Mellow, not unkindly. "Please. There. That's better. Now then: listen to me." And something, at that moment, seemed to happen to Henry

Mellow: to Mr. Brown he looked bigger, wider, and, somehow realer than he had been before. It was as if the business he was in had for a long time kept him from seeing people as real, and now, suddenly, he could again.

Henry Mellow said, "I've had a lot longer to think this out than you have, and besides, I don't think the way you do. I guess I don't think the way anybody does. So I've been told. But for what it's worth, here it is: If I tried to keep this thing and control it myself, I wouldn't live ten minutes. (What's the matter, Mr. Brown? Somebody else say that? I wouldn't doubt it.) Or I could just file it away and forget it; matter of fact, I tried that and I just couldn't forget it, because there's a lot of people dying now, and more could die in the future, for lack of it. I even thought of printing it up, in detail, and scattering it from a plane. But then, you know what I wrote about how many shepherds didn't look into how many dewdrops; that could happen again—probably would, and it's not a thing I could do thousands of times. So I've decided to do what I said—publish it in a magazine. But not in detail. I don't want anyone to think they stole it, and I don't want anyone to make a lot out of it and then come looking for me, either to eliminate me (that could happen) or to share it, because I don't want to share it with one person or two or a company—I want to share it with everybody, all the good that comes of it, all the bad. You don't understand that, do you, Mr. Brown?

"You're going to meet a doctor friend of mine in a minute who will give you something that will help you forget. It's quite harmless, but you won't remember any of this. So before you go, I just want to tell you one thing: there's another Mr. Brown downstairs. Mr. Brown X, he said you called him, and all he wanted was the process—not for himself, not for the Agency, but for his people; he said they *really* know how to get along with Nothing." He smiled. "And I don't want you to feel too badly about this, but your Agency's not as fast on its feet as you think it is. Last week I had a man with some sort of Middle European accent and a man who spoke Ukrainian and two orientals and a fellow with a beard from Cuba. Just thought I'd tell you. . . .

"So good-bye, Mr. Brown. You'll forget all about this talk, but maybe when you write a check and tear it in two getting it out of the book, or when you rip off a paper towel or a stamp and the perforations hold, something will tell you to stop a minute and think it through." He smiled and touched a second button on his intercom.

"Stand by, Doc."

"Ready," said the intercom.

Henry Mellow moved something under the edge of his desk and the visitor's chair dropped through the floor. In a moment it reappeared, empty. Henry Mellow touched another control, and the sheets of Nothing slid up and away, to await the next one.

So when it happens, don't just say Damn and forget it. Stop a minute and think it through. Somebody's going to change the face of the earth and it could be you.

Brownshoes

His name was Mensch; it once was a small joke between them, and then it became a bitterness. "I wish to God I could have you now the way you were," she said, "moaning at night and jumping up and walking around in the dark and never saying why, and letting us go hungry and not caring how we lived or how we looked. I used to bitch at you for it, but I never minded, not really. I held still for it. I would've, just for always, because with it all you did your own thing, you were a free soul."

"I've always done my own thing," said Mensch, "and I did so tell you why."

She made a disgusted sound. "Who could understand all that?" It was dismissal, an old one; something she had recalled and worked over and failed to understand for years, a thing that made tiredness. "And you used to love people—really love them. Like the time that kid wiped out the fire hydrant and the streetlight in front of the house and you fought off the fuzz and the schlock lawyer and the ambulance and everybody, and got him to the hospital and wouldn't let him sign the papers because he was dazed. And turning that cheap hotel upside down to find Victor's false teeth and bring them to him after they put him in jail. And sitting all day in the waiting room the time Mrs. What's-her-name went for her first throat cancer treatment, so you could take her home, you didn't even know her. There wasn't anything you wouldn't do for people."

"I've always done what I could. I didn't stop."

Scorn. "So did Henry Ford. Andrew Carnegie. The Krupp family. Thousands of jobs, billions in taxes for everybody. I know the stories."

"My story's not quite the same," he said mildly.

Then she said it all, without hate or passion or even much emphasis; she said in a burnt-out voice, "We loved each other and you walked out."

They loved each other. Her name was Fauna; it once was a small joke between them. Fauna the Animal and Mensch the Man, and the thing they had between them. "Sodom is a-cumen in," he misquoted Chaucer, "Lewd sing cuckold" (because she had a husband back there somewhere amongst the harpsichord lessons and the mildewed unfinished hooked rugs and the skeleton of a play and all the other abandoned projects in the attic of her life). Mensch was the first one she could have carried through, all the way. She was one of those people who waits for the right thing to come along and drops all others as soon as she finds out they aren't the main one. When someone like that gets the right thing, it's forever, and everyone says, my how you've changed. She hasn't changed.

But then when the right thing comes along, and it doesn't work out, she'll never finish anything again. Never.

They were both very young when they met and she had a little house back in the woods near one of those resort towns that has a reputation for being touristy-artsy-craftsy and actually does have a sprinkling of real artists in and around it. Kooky people are more than tolerated in places like that providing only that (a) they attract, or at least do not repel, the tourists and (b) they never make any important money. Nothing disturbs the people who really run a town like that more than an oddball who strikes it rich; people begin to listen to him, and that could change things. Fauna wasn't about to change things. She was a slender pretty girl who liked to be naked under loose floor-length gowns and take care of sick things as long as they couldn't talk—broken-wing birds and philodendrons and the like—and lots of music—lots of *kinds* of music; and cleverly doing things she wouldn't finish until the real thing came along. She had a solid title to the little house and a part-time job in the local frame shop; she was picturesque and undemanding and never got involved in marches and petitions and the like. She just believed in being kind to everyone around her and thought . . . well, that's not quite right. She hadn't ever thought it out all the way, but she *felt* that if you're kind to everyone the kindness will somehow spread over the world like a healing stain, and that's what you do about wars and greed and injustice. So she was an acceptable, almost approved fixture in the town even when they paved her dirt road and put the lamppost and fire hydrant in front of it.

Mensch came into this with long hair and a guitar strapped to his back, a head full of good books and a lot of very serious restlessness. He moved in with Fauna the day after she discovered his guitar was tuned like a lute. He had busy hands too, and a way of finishing what he started, yes, and making a dozen more like them—beautifully designed kitchen pads for shopping lists made out of hand-rubbed local woods, which used adding-machine rolls and had a hunk of hacksaw blade down at the bottom so you could neatly tear off a little or a lot, and authentic reproductions of fireplace bellows and apple-peelers and stuff like that which could be displayed on the shoppes (not stores, they were shoppes) on the village green, and bring in his share. Also he knew about transistors and double-helical gears and eccentric linkages and things like Wankels and fuel cells. He fiddled around a lot in the back room with magnets and axles and colored fluids of various kinds, and one day he had an idea and began fooling with scissors and cardboard and some metal parts. It was mostly frame and a rotor, but it was made of certain things in a certain way. When he put it together the rotor began to spin, and he suddenly understood it. He made a very slight adjustment and the rotor, which was mostly cardboard, uttered a shrill rising sound and spun so fast that the axle, a tenpenny nail, chewed right through the cardboard bearings and the rotor took off and flew across the room, showering little unglued metal bits. He made no effort to collect the parts, but stood up blindly and walked into the other room. Fauna took one look at him and ran to him and held him: what is it? what's the matter? but he just stood there looking stricken until the tears began rolling down his cheeks. He didn't seem to know it.

That was when he began moaning suddenly in the middle of the night, jumping up and walking around in the dark. When she said years later that he would never tell her why, it was true, and it wasn't, because what he told her was that he had something in his head so important that certain people would kill him to get it, and certain other people would kill him to suppress it, and that he wouldn't tell her what it was because he loved her and didn't want her in danger. She cried a lot and said he didn't trust her, and he said he did, but he wanted to take care of her, not throw her to the wolves. He also said—and this is what the moaning and nightwalking was all about—that the thing in his head could make the deserts bloom and could feed hungry people all over the world, but that if he let it loose it could be like a plague too, not because of what it was but because of what people would do with it; and the very first person who died because of it would die because of him, and he couldn't bear the idea of that. He really had a choice to make, but before he could make it he had to decide whether the death of one person was too great a price to pay for the happiness and security of millions, and then if the deaths of a thousand would be justified if it meant the end of poverty for all. He knew history and psychology and he had a mathematician's head as well as those cobbler's hands, and he knew damned well what would happen if he took this way or that. For example, he knew where he could unload the idea and all responsibility for it for enough money to keep him and Fauna—and a couple hundred close friends, if it came to that—in total luxury for the rest of their lives; all he would have to do would be to sign it away and see it buried forever in a corporate vault, for there were at least three industrial giants which would urgently bid against one another for the privilege.

Or kill him.

He also thought of making blueprints and scattering millions of copies over cities all over the world, and of finding good ethical scientists and engineers and banding them together into a firm which would manufacture and license the device and use it only for good things. Well you can do that with a new kind of rat-killer or sewing machine, but not with something so potent that it will change the face of the earth, eliminate hunger, smog, and the rape of raw materials—not when it will also eliminate the petro-chemical industry (except for dyes and plastics), the electric-power companies, the internal-combustion engine and everything involved in making it and fueling it, and even atomic energy for most of its purposes.

Mensch tried his very best to decide not to do anything at all about it, which was the moaning and nightwalking interval, and that just wouldn't work—the thing would not let him go. Then he decided what to do, and what he must do in order to do it. His first stop was at the town barbershop.

Fauna held still for this and for his getting a job at Flextronics, the town's light industry, which had government contracts for small computer parts and which was scorned by the town's art, literature and library segment. The regular hours appalled her, and although he acted the same (he certainly didn't look the same) around the house, she became deeply troubled. She had never seen so much money as he brought in every payday, and didn't want to, and for the first time in her life had to get stubborn about patching and improvising and doing without instead of being able to blame poverty for it. The reasons she found now for living that way seemed specious even to her, which only made her stubborn about it, and more of a kook than ever. Then he bought a car, which seemed to her an immorality of sorts.

What tore it was when somebody told her he had gone to the town-board meeting, which she had never done, and had proposed that the town pass ordinances against sitting on the grass on the village green, playing musical instruments on town thoroughfares, swimming at the town swimming hole after sundown, and finally, hiring more police. When she demanded an explanation he looked at her sadly for a long time, then would not deny it, would not discuss it, and moved out.

He got a clean room in a very square boarding house near the factory, worked like hell until he got his college credits straightened out, went to night school until he had another degree. He took to hanging around the Legion post on Saturday nights and drank a little beer and bought a lot of whiskey for other people. He learned a whole portfolio of dirty jokes and dispensed them carefully, two-thirds sex, one-third bathroom. Finally he took a leave of absence from his job, which was, by this time, section manager, and moved down the river to a college town where he worked full time on a postgraduate engineering degree while going to night school to study law. The going was very tough around then because he had to pinch every nickel to be able to make it and still keep his pants creased and his brown shoes shiny, which he did. He still found time to join the local church and become a member of the vestry board and a lay preacher, taking as his text the homilies from *Poor Richard's Almanac* and delivering them (as did their author) as if he believed every word.

When it was time he redesigned his device, not with cardboard and glue, but with machined parts that were 70 percent monkey-puzzle—mechanical motions that canceled each other out, and wiring which energized coils which shorted themselves out. He patented parts and certain group-ings of parts, and finally the whole contraption. He then took his degrees and graduate degrees, his published scholarly papers, his patents and his short haircut, together with a letter of introduction from his pastor, to a bank, and borrowed enough to buy into a failing company which made portable conveyor belts. His device was built into the drive segment, and he went on the road to sell the thing. It sold very well. It should. A six-volt automobile battery would load coal with that thing for a year without needing replacement or recharging, and no wonder, because the loading was being powered by that little black lump in the drive segment, which, though no bigger than a breadbox, and requiring no fuel, would silently and powerfully spin a shaft until the bearings wore out.

It wasn't too long before the competition was buying Mench's loaders and tearing them down to see where all that obscene efficiency was coming from. The monkey-puzzle was enough to defeat most of them, but one or two bright young men and a grizzled oldster or so were able to realize that they were looking at something no bigger than a breadbox which would turn a shaft indefinitely without fuel, and wonder what things would be like with this gadget under the hood of a car or in the nacelles of aircraft, or pumping water in the desert, or generating light and power 'way back in the hills and jungles without having to build roads or railways or to string power lines. Some of these men found their way to Mensch. Either he hired them and tied them up tight with ropes of gold and fringe benefits, or had them watched and dissuaded, or discredited, or, if need be, ruined.

Inevitably someone was able to duplicate the Mensch effect, but by that time Mensch had a whole office building full of lawyers with their pencils sharpened and their instructions ready. The shrewd operator who had duplicated the effect, and who had sunk everything he had and could borrow into retooling an engine factory for it, found himself in such a snarl of infringement, torts, ceases-and-desists, and prepaid royalty demands that he sold his plant at cost to Mensch and gratefully accepted a job managing it. And he was only the first.

The military moved in at about this point, but Mensch was ready for them and their plans to take over his patents and holdings as a national resource. He let himself be bunted higher and higher in the chain of command, while his refusals grew stronger and stronger and the threats greater and greater, until he emerged at the top in the company of the civilian who commanded them all. This meeting was brought about by a bishop, for never in all these busy years did Mensch overlook his weekly duty at the church of his choice, nor his tithes, nor his donations of time for an occasional Vacation Bible School or picnic or bazaar. And Mensch, on this pinnacle of wealth, power and respectability, was able to show the President the duplicate set of documents he had placed in a Swiss bank, which, on the day his patents were preempted by the military, would donate them to research institutes in Albania and points north and east. That was the end of that.

The following year a Mensch-powered car won the Indy. It wasn't as fast as the Granatelli entry; it just voomed around and around the brickyard without making any stops at all. There was, of course, a certain amount of static for a while, but the inevitable end was that the automobile industry capitulated, and with it the fossil-fuel people. Electric light and power had to follow and, as the gas and steam and diesel power sources obsolesce and are replaced by Mensch prime movers, the atomic plants await their turn.

It was right after the Indianapolis victory that Mensch donated his blueprints to Albania anyway—after all, he had never said he wouldn't—and they showed up about the same time in Hong Kong and quickly reached the mainland. There was a shrill claim from the Soviet Union that the Mensch Effect had been discovered in the nineteenth century by Siolkovsky, who had set it aside because he was more interested in rockets, but even the Russians couldn't keep that up for long without laughing along with the audience, and they fell to outstripping all other nations in development work. No monkey-puzzle on earth can survive this kind of effort—monkey-puzzles need jungles of patent law to live and thrive—and it was not long before the Soviets (actually, it was a Czech scientist, which is the same thing, isn't it? Well, the Soviets said it was) were able to proclaim that they had improved and refined the device to a simple frame supporting one moving part, the rotor: each made, of course, of certain simple substances which, when assembled, began to work. It was, of course, the same frame and rotor with which Mensch, in terror and tears, had begun his long career, and the Czech, that is, Soviet "refinement" was, like all else, what he had predicted and aimed himself toward.

For now there wasn't a mechanics magazine in the world, nor hardly a tinkerer's workshop anywhere, that didn't begin turning out Mensch rotors. Infringements occurred so widely that even Mensch's skyscraperful of legal-eagles couldn't have begun to stem the flood. And indeed they did not try, because—

For the second time in modern history (the first was an extraordinary man named Kemal Ataturk) a man of true national-dictator stature set his goal, achieved it, and abdicated. It didn't matter one bit to Mensch that the wiser editorialists, with their knowledgeable index fingers placed alongside their noses, were pointing out that he had defeated himself, shattered his own empire by extending its borders, and that by releasing his patents into the public domain he was making an empty gesture to the inevitable. Mensch knew what he had done, and why, and what other people thought of it just did not matter.

"What does matter," he said to Fauna in her little house by the old fire hydrant and the quaint streetlamp, "is that there isn't a kraal in Africa or a hamlet in Asia that can't pump water and plow land and heat and light its houses by using a power plant simple enough to be built by any competent mechanic anywhere. There are little ones to rock cradles and power toys and big ones to light whole cities. They pull trains and sharpen pencils, and they need no fuel. Already desalted

Mediterranean water is pouring into the northern Sahara; there'll be whole new cities there, just as there were five thousand years ago. In ten years the air all over the earth will be measurably cleaner, and already the demand for oil is down so much that offshore drilling is almost completely stopped. 'Have' and 'have-not' no longer mean what they once meant, because everyone has access to cheap power. And that's why I did it, don't you see?" He really wanted very much to make her understand.

"You cut your hair," she said bitterly. "You wore those awful shoes and went to church and got college degrees and turned into a—a typhoon."

"Tycoon," he corrected absently. "Ah, but Fauna, listen: remember when we were kids, how there were protests and riots in the universities? Think of just one small aspect of that. Suppose a crowd of students wanted to take the administration building—how did they do it? They swarmed up the roads and sidewalks, didn't they? Now—oh hear me out!" for she was beginning to shake her head, open her mouth to interrupt. "Up the roads and sidewalks. Now when those roads and walks were built, the planners and architects didn't put them there to be used that way, did they? But that doesn't matter—when the mob wants to get to the administration building, they take the road that's there. And that's all I did. The way to get what I wanted was short hair, was brown shoes, was published postgraduate papers, was the banks and businesses and government and all of those things that were already there for me to use."

"You didn't need all that. I think you just wanted to move things and shake things and be in the newspapers and history books. You could've made your old motor right here in this house and showed it to people and sold it and stayed here and played the lute, and it would have been the same thing."

"No, there you're wrong," said Mensch. "Do you know what kind of a world we live in? We live in a world where, if a man came up with a sure cure for cancer, and if that man

174

were found to be married to his sister, his neighbors would righteously burn down his house and all his notes. If a man built the most beautiful tower in the country, and that man later begins to believe that Satan should be worshipped, they'll blow up his tower. I know a great and moving book written by a woman who later went quite crazy and wrote crazy books, and nobody will read her great one any more. I can name three kinds of mental therapy that could have changed the face of the earth, and in each case the men who found it went on to insane Institutes and so-called religions and made fools of themselves—dangerous fools at that—and now no one will look at their really great early discoveries. Great politicians have been prevented from being great statesmen because they were divorced. And I wasn't going to have the Mensch machine stolen or buried or laughed at and forgotten just because I had long hair and played the lute. You know, it's easy to have long hair and play the lute and be kind to people when everyone else around you is doing it. It's a much harder thing to be the one who does it first, because then you have to pay a price, you get jeered at and they throw stones and shut you out."

"So you joined them," she accused.

"I used them," he said flatly. "I used every road and path that led to where I was going, no matter who built it or what it was built for."

"And you paid your price," she all but snarled. "Millions in the bank, thousands of people ready to fall on their knees if you snap your fingers. Some price. You could have had love."

He stood up then and looked at her. Her hair was much thinner now, but still long and fine. He reached for it, lifted some. It was white. He let it go.

He thought of fat Biafran babies and clean air and unpolluted beaches, cheaper food, cheaper transportation, cheaper manufacturing and maintenance, more land to lessen the pressures and hysteria during the long slow process of population control. What had moved him to deny himself so much, to rebel, to move and shake and shatter the status quo the way he had, rather than conforming—conforming!—to long hair and a lute? *You could have had love.*

"But I did," he said; and then, knowing she would never, could never understand, he got in his silent fuelless car and left.

Uncle Fremmis

"My God!" I cried, "it's . . . it can't be." Then, a little awed by the fact that my voice didn't echo in those wide endless corridors—well hell, they had carpeting an inch and a half thick—I added almost shyly, "Uncle Fremmis?"

"Shore is, son," he said.

I must say, I was shocked.

Uncle Fremmis—actually he was my mother's uncle—was a hardbitten, easy-laughing, gray-headed man when I was merely toddling. When I was grown, and before I left the Lake country (there's mostly hills there, but they call it the lake country) Uncle Fremmis was still a hard-bitten, easy-laughing gray-headed man. He lived pretty much by himself at one end of a hogback with a kind of pond—what it was was a crooked wide place in a creek—on one side and a deep foggy valley on the other. It was a valley nobody wanted, I guess—even now it's the same way it always was, and Uncle Fremmis used to like to watch the light come before the sun did, and the rabbits and all, and squirrels red and gray and bobolinks and the deer that would gaze on the steep grass until the sun burned the mist away. He used to hang around town a lot and was a very popular man although as far as I know he was never really close to anybody. When he needed staples he'd turn his hand to everything—splitting wood with a go-devil, or digging wells, or swamping (which means anything you want it to mean) around the lumber mill. Flour and salt and needles—that's the kind of stuff he'd buy. Yellow soap and levis and every few years a bucket and an ax, a whetstone, a pitcher.

He made enemies; they were always the same kind of man. The first one that I remember was a blacksmith. He rightly hated Uncle Fremmis, and came up to him on the street one day with his hand out, and Uncle Fremmis grinned his quick grin and took it, and the blacksmith snatched him off his feet and stomped him, which didn't do either one of them any good because folks stopped dealing with him pretty much except when they had to, and when folks like that want to get along without having to, they can go a long way. I recall one farmer used a one-wheeled hay rake for close to three years rather than have that smith fix a busted axle cap. The right side of the rake rode on a skid like a travois, that the farmer made out of old spring leaves. Uncle Fremmis never did anything to get back at the blacksmith except to stand in the middle of the street laughing the day the smith nailed up the FOR SALE sign on his shop.

The years rolled by slower in that country, somehow, than other places, but they brought new things all the same. The workhorses went the way of the buggy horses and everybody had a tractor, and it was old Pidgeon, that owned the gas station, who got to bad-mouthing Uncle Fremmis so much. Uncle Fremmis paid that no mind at all until Pidgeon bought into the general store and tried to stop Uncle Fremmis' credit, because things were up and down with Uncle Fremmis and when they were down the credit made a lot of difference, and never once in his life did he leave a bill unpaid (nor run up more than maybe forty dollars worth of them). When word got around about that, business fell off so bad at the gas station and the tractor shop that was part of it that old Pidgeon was hard put to it to pay his bills. Tractors just didn't hardly break down any more and when they did, somehow there was always a neighbor to borrow one from, and some of the horses still left around came out of pasture and went back to work again. Before you know it old Pidgeon had to sell out his piece of the general store and then Uncle Fremmis had his credit back again. That gas station and the repair shop never did do real well until old Pidgeon sold out, either.

And when I was in the high school there was a walleyed young man name of Skutch who opened up an electric and radio place. He did real good until the second time he tried to hurt Uncle Fremmis. The first time he said it was an accident, when he hired him to help out one afternoon and told him to hold onto a wire and then did something that gave Uncle Fremmis such a shock it laid him out and he swallowed his tongue, he really did, and that would have been all for Uncle Fremmis if Dr. Weiss hadn't happened by and hooked the tongue back with his finger and brought him around. The second time Skutch went after Uncle Fremmis with his Essex Terraplane automobile; he said that was an accident too, but if it was it was an accident that went a quarter mile along Beasley Road and out into Roudenbush's cornfield with Uncle Fremmis jumping and ducking like a jackrabbit until Skutch saw Roudenbush sitting there on his tractor watching, so he quit. After that Skutch's trade fell off real bad and if you had a business in town and you bought from Skutch, somehow your business would fall off too, so Skutch didn't last long.

Whenever Uncle Fremmis needed more than just his staples, he would dowse. He was a waterfinder; he'd whittle you a piece of apple (some dowsers use willow, but Uncle Fremmis always cut a little Y off a green apple tree) and walk around with it in his hands, and where it bent down sharp he'd say dig, and there was your well. He only did this three times that I can remember, and it cost five hundred dollars a time, and he got it because his deal was real straight: if he said dig and there was no water, you didn't pay him. (The price of the digging was your gamble.) All those three times he was right and got his money. He got kind of famous around there

179

for that and had all the offers he could have wanted, but he didn't want them. He didn't believe in the income tax and never would earn more than five hundred dollars in a year.

He never did marry that I know of. He visited around a little, and it's a measure of where he stood in the Lake country that although they like to gossip as much as anybody anywhere, they let Uncle Fremmis' business be his business, except maybe one or another of the ladies would nudge the latest one a little and slip her a wink and make her blush. So all in all he didn't need much more than he made helping out here and there, except for something special, or to catch up on the store account after a bed spell.

One of the something specials was a Model 1-NC quarter-ton panel truck. You probably don't remember the 1-NC. It was the last four-cylinder wheels that Henry ever made. (I don't count the Jeep because that wasn't Henry's to begin with.) The truck had this funny little corn popper up front and right behind it the biggest four-speed gearbox you ever saw, so that in low-low it would walk up the side of a billboard if you could find some way to make it stick on. The speedometer only went up to sixty which if you ever drove a 1-NC is just childish, like little kids betting a million; downhill, flat out, and with a following wind a 1-NC could maybe go forty-three. Anyway Uncle Fremmis fell in love with one and found water for some dude over in Clearwater and took the money and bought the truck. He got Ed Varney to take out the corn-popper and put in a rebuilt V-8 from Sears and Roebuck, and a two-speed rear axle off a Reo. He got Ed to do it because with mechanical things Uncle Fremmis was the best water dowser and well digger around, if you see what I mean. Anyway that old 1-NC, peeling green paint and rust spots and all, turned into something like a buzz bomb with the wings chopped. Riding in it with Uncle Fremmis was a real hairy experience. The speedo needle would go right away up to the sixty and hit a pin there, and after that you could see it bend. The suspension was narrow-gauge and the tires were 6-15's and the shocks were long gone and pure decoration. The body was very high and narrow and kind of humped and when it got to swaying a bit it would pick up both left wheels and then both right wheels and you wouldn't know what that thumping was until you asked Uncle Fremmis and he told you. On the other hand, no matter how useless Uncle Fremmis was with a wrench, he was a fine artist with the wheel and he never did flip that thing. Nobody ever knew how fast it would go. He let it out on the State highway one afternoon and a state patrolman on a hog chased him a ways and then let him go because he was afraid to catch him; he said later that what was sure to happen he just couldn't bear to see, but anyway he clocked him at eighty-seven and caught him on the way back. Uncle Fremmis, because he was Uncle Fremmis, wound up without a ticket and, for an hour and a half, with the policeman's head under the hood and down under, looking up at that monstrous rear axle. That cop later won a NASCAR finals, and used to tell about Uncle Fremmis and how he started him on the hot wheels, but that's another story. Anyway it was that truck that led me to understand about Uncle Fremmis.

I had a girl, I mean I meant to have her, who had a mother who had a cow who had a calf who didn't like me, I mean the mother; and I knew I'd never so much as get up to the barricades, let alone cross them, unless I could make the mother glad at me. Well she sold this calf to a farmer over to West Fork who wouldn't come for it and she wouldn't bring it without two dollars extra, so there it stood, her wanting the money and him wanting the calf and her saying to come for it and him saying bring it and her saying for two dollars and him saying no, so I borrowed the truck.

I borrowed Uncle Fremmis' truck, and you know I never did get that calf over to West Fork. I never got the calf. I didn't get but halfway to her mother's place and then turned that thing around somehow and got it back to Uncle Fremmis. You see, it had a gas pedal on it that was hinged at the back, down on the floor, and the pin had long ago worked out of the hinge. With a working hinge the pedal would push a wire which would feed the gas. With the pin out the pedal would lay over sideways every time you put your foot down, and if you were in anything higher than low gear, the motor would stall. You've balanced a broom on the end of your finger—everybody has. Well that's what you had to do with your foot on that gas pedal, except you don't move your foot around with the precision of a finger. It might seem like a small thing the way I say it, but you just try it with a big V-8 up front and a 2-speed axle behind and a banging, swaying zombie (remember a zombie is the walking dead) of an obsolete panel truck all around you, and your head full of plans about doing the calf bit and collecting your just reward. I was like frustrated.

Uncle Fremmis just laughed a lot. But I began to realize what I guess I had known for a long time—Uncle Fremmis was not like other people. I mean he didn't even have a lock on that truck, just a toggle switch. He just had a—

He had a way of making things work.

Don't think that means he could fix things. It doesn't mean that. He couldn't fix anything but dinner. Well, here's what I mean: he had an old radio in the house, a car radio he ran off a spare battery he would switch every now and then with the one in the truck. Sometimes the radio would hang onto a station all right but something had got old in its guts, and it would drop down to a whisper and then when you turned it up so you could hear it, it would suddenly cut in so loud it would make you bite your tongue. Uncle Fremmis would run his hand over it, back and forth and up and back again, and then the hand would stop, and maybe move over a quarter inch, and then *whammo*, he'd fetch it a stinging blow with the heel of his hand, and it would be all right again for a month.

Which is also why he had so many friends, and a number of real bad enemies. Uncle Fremmis was just not quite like other people.

It was around this time—the girl with the mother and the

cow and the calf and all that—that I started to get into trouble. Life was so simple and good then that I didn't know how simple and good it was. I guess it began when I borrowed twenty dollars from Sam Pritchard and promised to pay him in two weeks and couldn't. I borrowed thirty from old Joe at the barbershop so I could pay Sam, but I had to have a little for myself. When it came time to pay Joe, I went to Sam again. He was willing, but he only had twenty, so I was ten short. I needed a little for myself so I borrowed twenty from Hank Johanssen, and about then things began to get complicated. I somehow got Sam and Joe down to thirty apiece after a while, and carried it back and forth between them for about six weeks. Then I couldn't pay Hank and he got real mad at me and told Joe to watch out for me, so the next time I asked Joe for twenty he just said no. I thought that over for a while and then had a bright idea, and I still think it was a good one: I said to Joe he should give Sam thirty dollars, and in two weeks Sam could give him thirty dollars, and I'd just be out of it and could concentrate on Hank. And he threw me out of the barbershop.

So then I thought of Uncle Fremmis, and I thought this: (a) there was no way of knowing how much Uncle Fremmis had, so maybe he would have fifty bucks; (b) he didn't really need anything, so it would probably be all right if he didn't get it back; and (c) he'd lent me his truck once, hadn't he, so why wouldn't he lend me money? I went straight up to the hogback and the pole-and-shake house made of one hundred percent repairs on a tar-paper lean-to from thirty years ago, and it was there all right but he wasn't, and neither was the 1-NC. I asked around and found he'd left in it and nobody knew where, and he never came back at all that I know of. I remember feeling real mad at Uncle Fremmis, deserting me like that.

I was around town for a while after that but things got much too complicated. I never could figure out how it all happened, but it got so I couldn't borrow anything anymore, and if I couldn't borrow, how was I going to pay anyone? It was a lot simpler to go to the city and let them all work it out for themselves.

I did much better in the city, by which I mean in three years I owed about twelve thousand. I kept thinking about the guy who founded one of the most successful motel chains in the United States. When he was a teen-ager he made up his mind to *owe* a million by the time he was twenty-five. He made it and became a big wheel. I guess I just didn't have his class. It was taking me a lot longer and the world seems to be kind of intolerant of guys who take long.

So I was at a party, brought there by a chick who thought some other people might think I was funny (because you can't get the country out of the boy) and I zeroed in on a guy in a silk suit who had an office in this skyscraper. It was in the part of a skyscraper they call Towers, which is up on top where they have these thick carpets in all the hallways and you have to change elevators before you get there and the Tower elevator has a plug-ugly running it and you better have a reason. I had a reason but I also had Silk Suit's card which I hoped he was still drunk enough to remember how drunk he was when he gave it to me, and I got into his office and hit him for half a G, and when he asked me what for, I couldn't think of a good enough reason so he threw me out. Which was what was happening and why I was there when I ran into Uncle Femmis. "What," I said to him, "the hell are you doing here, Uncle Fremmis?" He was dressed in blue Lee work pants and shirt with keys on a belt clip. He wasn't carrying a broom or wheeling a waxing machine but he might as well. But it really was Uncle Fremmis, all those miles and years away from the hogback, the valley full of morning mist, the crooked pond; most of all away from town where all those people used to like him so much. Need him.

"Don't have time to tell you, son," he said. "Come along and I'll show you."

He hurried me along the corridor. His hand on my arm was rock-hard and his movements quick and definite; the years

184

hadn't changed him one bit. I don't mean the years since he had left town; I mean the years since I first toddled up to his kneecap and I looked up at that quick smile.

We passed doors with polite little names on them—most of them I'd seen in the papers at one time or another, you know, dollar-a-year men called in to advise the President, men's names that have become trademarks like Eveready or Birdseye, and then the ones I hadn't seen before doubtless because of my own ignorance or because they were so big and powerful nobody even knew they existed—they just ran things. One name I did know, though, and it stopped me cold and I said "Wow." *Semlar E. Warburg, M.D., A.P.A.* "Wow. He's the one who—"

"That's the one," said Uncle Fremmis. We were talking about the most famous psychiatrist in the whole entire world, a shrink who had written books and who had a "school"—that means a special way of doing his thing where whole colleges full of graduates go out and hang up shingles and do the same—or try to. Years back he would be called once in a while in law cases; he was far above that now, you might as well call in the Pope or J. Edgar. Uncle Fremmis unhooked his keys and turned those bright eyes on me: you could feel it when he did that, they like had points like a fence staple. "Now you listen to me, son," he said, in the way that made you listen to him, "what you're goin' to see you keep to yourself, right? And if you have to talk, keep your voice down."

I said I would, and he unlocked a narrow door next one down from Dr. Warburg's. I thought it was a broom closet until we were inside and he reached past me and closed the door. It locked with a heavy click. It was dark as the inside of a coal miner's lunch box. "Wait a bit until you can see," he said quietly, and I did, and sure enough, pretty soon I could make out that we were in a dark narrow corridor with what felt like foam rubber underfoot. "Wait now," he said when I was about to ask a question; he seemed to know it.

Suddenly there was a blaze of light a few feet ahead. It

made me jump. Uncle Fremmis said, "As the cigar said to the cigarette, son, we got here just in the nicotine." He nudged me painfully in the ribs and then said, "No foolin', I cut that too fine. He likes me to be here a half hour ahead." He waved me toward the light.

It looked like a square window of plate glass set in the wall. Through it I saw a woman seated in an armless easy chair, half-turned toward me, and not three feet away. I couldn't help myself, I ducked back out of the way before she could see me. Uncle Fremmis chuckled quietly. "Don't let that worry you, son. That there's one of those one-way mirrors. Long as it's dark in here it looks like a mirror in there. She can't see you." Reassured, I looked again.

On a low table six feet away from the woman—a well-dressed woman with that harried look that people with money seem to carry like a club membership—was a black box with three knobs and a shiny reflector about the size of a salad plate standing on edge. In the center of the reflector was what looked like a radio tube. Adjusting the dials, with a note pad in his hand, was a middle-aged man.

"That's him," said Uncle Fremmis.

"That's who?"

"The great man," grinned Uncle Fremmis. "Doctor Warburg."

I stared with disbelief. No goatee, no Austrian pipe, no funny European clothes. Just a man. "What's that gadget?"

"A BWS. Brain-wave synchronizer. It flashes. You turn those knobs, it makes it flash however often you want it to, as bright as you want it to."

"What's it for?"

"The way he explains it to me, everybody's brain has a certain kind of pulsebeat. The first time somebody comes here, he spends an hour or so finding out what it is. He writes that down, and sets the machine for it. After that, all he has to do is switch it on and it switches the person off."

"You mean like hypnotizes them?"

"Not 'like,' son—it does hypnotize 'em, in thirty, forty seconds instead of the thirty, forty minutes of hocus-pocus-your-eyes-are-gettin'-heavy."

"Then what?"

"Once they go under, Doc tells 'em they're goin' to dis-remember everything that happens until he says to wake up."

"And what happens?"

"Me," said Uncle Fremmis with some enjoyment. Before I could say anything to this, the man in the other room switched on the little machine. The tube lit up, not too bright, in a series of flashes of orange light. Each flash was probably no more than a hundredth of a second and the flashes came . . . I don't know how frequently. Something slower than a steady light, something faster than a flicker. I became aware that Uncle Fremmis was watching me intently.

"Son?"

"What?"

"It's all right. Just wondered if it had got to you. Isn't much chance that you and her, or any two people, have exactly the same frequency with the brain wave, but if you did, that thing would put you under 'fore you could say Boo. 'Course, you're not gettin' what she's gettin'—the reflector's givin' it to her head on. Whup! There she goes."

In the other room, we could see the woman's eyelids droop. They didn't quite close. She sat relaxed with her hands on her lap, staring straight in front of her. Dr. Warburg passed his hand close to her eyes and she didn't blink. He leaned close and appeared to be telling her something; at length she nodded slowly.

The doctor looked straight at us and beckoned.

"Back off out of the way," said Uncle Fremmis, "both when I go in there and when I come out. I don't think the doc'd be too happy about somebody in here with me," and he gave me a little shove back and turned a knob under the "window," which was my first intimation that it was really a door. It opened and let him into the room with the lady and the doctor, and he closed it behind him. I got where I could see again.

The doctor waved a hand and Uncle Fremmis answered something; they both laughed. I could see this was a very familiar thing to them. The doctor made a "she's-all-yours" kind of gesture and Uncle Fremmis stepped over to the lady. She didn't seem to notice him at all—just kept staring at the little machine. Or maybe she didn't even see it any more. It made no difference when Uncle Fremmis passed between it and her.

He moved around her, looking at her, looking for something. Then he began to put his hands on her, or so close to her that he was almost touching; I couldn't be sure. I thought she might hit him for it or draw back, or the doctor would stop him, but no. After a while—oh, a minute and a half—his hands settled around her head and face, and finally over her left ear. He moved his left fingertips back and forth an inch or so, and they settled on a certain spot and rested there, and then shifted just a little, little bit. Uncle Fremmis seemed to be concentrating real hard. When he found exactly what he seemed to be looking for, he raised his right hand up and back . . . the whole thing reminded me of something I'd seen before, but I didn't know what . . . then he fetched her such a lick alongside of the head I bit my tongue, and with the pain came the memory of that old car radio he had in his shack that wouldn't work right till he hit it a certain way in a certain place.

The lady's head rocked a bit but otherwise she just sat there, looking at the blinking light. Uncle Fremmis made the O sign for "OK" with his thumb and forefinger, grinned at the doctor and came back to me. I got out of the way as he opened the little door and came back into the secret corridor and shut it again. The whole thing hadn't taken more than two minutes.

We watched together while the doctor shut off the little machine and bent close to the lady, talking. We couldn't hear him but I could tell he was bringing her out of it. At first she just blinked slowly and began to raise a hand to put it against her head where she'd been hit, but the doc caught both her hands and went on talking until she was fully awake and looking at him. Then she smiled. It was a real nice smile, all that harried, harrassed look gone from her. Really gone. It was a nice smile.

Head close to mine as we watched, Uncle Fremmis said in my ear, "You always used to be a bright boy, son. What do you think happened?"

I didn't know what to think. I said, "You'll laugh at me."

"No." That's one of the smallest words there is, but he packed a heap into it. He wouldn't laugh at me. So I said the crazy thing that had crept into my head. I said, "You hit her just the way you used to with that old radio you had."

He sounded like he really admired me. "Oh, you are a bright one." And he patted my shoulder. Then he asked me how things were going back home.

It happens I'd been back for a week or so three months ago so I told him. The Lake country wasn't the same any more, like the twentieth century had got there at last altogether, not just a bit here and a piece there. I told him the way you do with down-home folks away from home, you know— who'd sold out and who had to get married and what happened to the church clock. He soaked it all in; I thought he looked sad. While I was talking the doctor in the other room got the lady up and they walked out together and the doc switched out the lights in there, and it was dark again in the corridor. Uncle Fremmis made no move to leave, so I went on talking in the dark. I said I didn't think I'd go back to the town again any more, ever; it wasn't really all that different from any other town now.

Just then the light came on again and we saw the doctor bringing in another one, and I recognized this one right away. He was a United States senator, been one for years. The doctor sat him down and reset the knobs on the little machine and put him under, and then Uncle Fremmis slipped out there and—and fixed him. Or not 'fixed him'—as he told me later, you couldn't call what he did 'fixing'. It's something else there's no real word for; Uncle Fremmis didn't know how to fix things, not really. This time there was no feeling around either; he went straight to the old Senator and lifted up the Senator's left hand to about shoulder high and snapped it down so hard I thought it might come off at the shoulder. If the doctor hadn't been hanging on tight I do believe he'd have tumbled the old feller right off the chair. Then he came back to me and we went on chatting while the doctor turned off the machine and brought the Senator around and led him out.

"It's my fault," Uncle Fremmis said sadly when he got back to me. "I mean about the town. It was me made it the way it was. Kep' it the way it was. I didn't mean to do it; I didn't know. It was Doc Warburg there made me realize it. And then it's my fault that things have changed so, too. To this day I don't know which was best."

"I don't know what you're talking about. I got to say, I liked it the way it was."

"The way it was was a backwater," he said sharply. I could see this whole thing meant a lot to him. "If a thing's alive it's got to change. If it stops changing it could be a lot of things—fun to be with or funny to look at or something for college folks to study, but it ain't alive no more, and a town's like a person, it has a right to be alive and grow and change and nobody should stop it."

"You mean you stopped it? How could you stop it?"

"Well, I made things work. I mean like that old lawnmower of Artie Backer's, with the kerosene motor. I used to go over to Artie's every six weeks during the warm weather and kick it. Wasn't nobody that knew where to kick it or how hard but me, and for me it worked. Old Mrs. Roudenbush, she had a meat grinder that would jam up so she couldn't turn it 'less I took holt of the crank and shook it just so."

And it all came back in a flood—Wertenbaker's tractor and Samuel's windmill pump and the church clock and dozens, scores, hundreds of other things, big and little, and Uncle Fremmis, drifting around town, knowing everybody and what everybody had that didn't work right, and making it go. Alarm clocks and sewing machines and the farm stuff—seeders and harrows and spreaders and drills.

And I recalled the blacksmith who had tromped him on the village street and the electrician who'd tried twice to wipe out Uncle Fremmis, and I began to understand those things, why they were enemies and why the town rode 'em out. When the light in the other room came on and I could see him again I looked at him with brand new eyes, like I'd never seen him before. I watched while he went in to the doctor and that famous preacher you've all seen on the TV, and while the preacher slumped there staring into the blinking light, Uncle Fremmis fetched him a hell of a clip between the shoulder blades with the heel of his hand.

When he came back I asked him how he'd happened to come here, and he told me about it, setting up in his cabin watching the rabbits in the steep meadow one early morning, and he seen somebody moving around down by the crooked pond on the other side of the hogback. "A nippy morning, it was," he said, "and there was this man in his shirt sleeves wading into the water so I knew right away something was haywire and I scrambled down there. There was a monstrous big Cadillac parked on the west bank and this feller was heading out for deep water with a kind of I-can't-see-you look on his face. I brought him back. He didn't want to come. Much bigger'n me, so when talkin' didn't help and pullin' and haulin' didn't help I did the only thing I could think of . . . hell, I didn't even think. I mean it was like he wasn't a man at all but a threshin' machine with a jammed conveyor or some kid's old Mickey Mouse watch. I mean it was a tight thing, son, he could've dragged me into the deep water too, so all I did was the only thing I could do. I hit him a certain way." He prodded me on the right side, a little above the waist. " 'Long about here, and it straightened him right out. He stopped dead an' looked at me like wonderin' where he was at, so we waded ashore and come up to my place and drank a lot of coffee and dried out in front of the fire. Here comes the Maestro."

We looked through the mirror and saw one of the world's biggest orchestra leaders, so corny even country people laugh at him but what the hell, if you like bubbles and music ex-act-ly on-the-beat, you got a right. Uncle Fremmis went in there and turned the guy's right foot half around and held it between his knees while he reached up and gave him a kind of karate chop on the neck, not too hard. When he came back he went on, "We talked all that day an' into the next night, me and the doc there. He's a big man, son, and I don't mean money and I don't mean all the books he's wrote and all. He's a big man with a clear head who ain't afraid to look at the truth even if the truth looks crazy. He told me about how it is in his line of work, how hard it is to rub up against so many people's nuttiness without it rubs off on them, and how the load of nuttiness he'd been carryin' just got so big over the years that one day somethin' snapped an' he took off in his big shiny Cadillac an' just drove an' drove till he wound up in the early mornin' lookin' at water, an' he just promptly waded in to drown himself. Yeah. He told me straight. And what I'd done when I hit him like that cleared the whole thing up for him somehow, made him see it all, made him work again like a ol' sewing machine or school bus or whatever. So he asked me a lot about me, an' we got into this thing about me not lettin' the town grow up natural. It made me feel real bad. Then he said for me to come to the city an' help him, an' he left, an' I thought it over for a couple days an' jumped into my truck an' took off."

"And now you fix people instead of things."

He snorted. "I don't fix nothing, son. I never did. I can't. It's like Artie Backer's lawn mower—what I did I had to do again every six weeks. Sometimes I could make things go for a year or more, sometimes a week. Each one's different. Same with these folks here. They all have to come back sooner or later, when the worn-out part inside, whatever it is, starts to act up. Dr. Warburg, I got to hit him like that about every nine months."

"What about the blinking light thing? Window dressing?"

I think that bugged him. "Window dressing hell. Do you think these people would hold still for what I do if they knowed it was me doin' it? That machine, and the way Warburg uses it, just makes it so they never see me."

"What do you need him for, Uncle Fremmis? My God, you could set up shop for yourself and make a mint."

"I don't want a mint, son. Never did. Anyway, who would want to go see a crazy old man to git slapped in the chops when they started to act crazy or couldn't cut the mustard any more?"

"A lot of people. Word gets out . . . you'd make a—"

"*These* people wouldn't. An' that's the big thing, son. These people are the big ones. These people are the ones who make things go. Only thing is, they git worn-out after a bit and it kind of poisons the things they do. Everybody says the world's goin' to hell in a handbasket, but it won't if we can keep enough of the top ones straightened out. There ain't many really top ones—never was. And we ain't got 'em all, but we're workin' on it. An' it strikes me that's a lot more use than keepin' a sewing machine running just because it belonged to somebody's granny, or to help a pinchpenny keep a ol' pump instead of buyin' a new one an' helpin' keep work an' jobs comin'."

I began to see a number of things, but one took my attention like a bikini in a hotel lobby, and that was, Uncle Fremmis was standing right next to a classic buck. "Uncle Fremmis," I said, "I need five thousand dollars."

Well I won't go into all the talk we had then while he asked me what I'd been doing and how I'd been living, but with him you couldn't duck straight questions and you couldn't make things look good when they weren't. When he was done asking and I was done telling I felt like something you shovel out of a cowbarn.

He looked at me for a long time and then heaved a deep

breath. "Tell you what, son," he said, "I'll do what I can for you. It won't take but a minute. We won't use no gadget box because between you and me we don't need it. Only I got to tell you up front, you ain't goin' to enjoy it, I ain't goin' to enjoy it, and you'll have to come back for more every once in a while—you'll know when."

"Do I get my five G's?" was all I could think of.

He clapped me heartily on the shoulder. It was real affection, and I could have cried. "You sure do, and more. All you want."

I said, "Then fire away."

So then and there, in the dark corridor, he ran his hands over me. They hardly touched, like butterflies. I heard him kind of grunt, and he moved his hands a bit more and they rested.

"Come on," he said. He took me out to the hallway outside. He looked up and down and there was nobody out there. So he did his thing, and you better believe it, it was one hell of a jolt. Oh my but he is a strong old man.

I went out that day and got a job. I did fine. I'm doing fine. And every once in a while, when I know it's time, I go back and see Uncle Fremmis. I know it's time when I begin to think I can't get along another day without borrowing money. Then I go back to him and he fetches me another good swift kick in the ass.

The Patterns Of Dorne

The dart was a miracle of miniaturized precision. A tiny sliver of a thing, it contained a laser generator, a proximity device, and a destruct mechanism so efficient that it would, on the instant, separate all its parts down to the molecular level. It would deliver to its target that one brief blast of intolerable heat, from close and lethal range, and would then cease to exist. A dissection of the murdered man would reveal the almost microscopic puncture burn—but then the exit wound would be almost identical and everything between them cooked into a sort of soup. There would be no marks on anything behind or around the victim; even the bright glare of almost-solar heat would be concealed within the victim's body, and as he fell, he must turn one way or the other; who could reconstruct the trajectory?

The little gun designed to throw the dart was equally a miracle—so small that it was dwarfed by the telescope mounted at its top. The propellant was a series of crypto-cryogenic solenoid rings, silent and lightless, wound with tens of thousands of turns of all but invisible, superconductive wire. In the 'scope was a complete light-amplification system, with automatic range-coupling with the focus. Anything found at the intersection of the radiant crosshairs and brought into focus was going to be killed. And all of it, gun and missiles, was made of materials well below the allowable error of the finest detection devices, and demountable into small unnoticeable parts which could be, which had been, distributed in and around the neatly fitted uniform of a Senior Lieutenant in the Leader's Guard. The Leader was Dorne, and in the bright image in the 'scope was the open balcony door of Dorne's suite, and all that was lacking to complete the picture, to complete this careful plan, was the appearance in it of Dorne's famous face.

The stone room in which the Lieutenant leaned yearning into his 'scope was more suited, perhaps, to the fifteenth century than to the twenty-first, with its ironbound oaken door and its single arrow-slit window. It was tomb-dark except for the tiny spot of light in the eyepiece, and empty except for half a lifetime's worth of hate and purpose and absolute certainty . . . and now, and now it was complete; now there was a shadow-flicker in the door across the inner courtyard, now it swung back and the face on the coins, the face of stamps and placards and statues and Government edicts, the great gentle-seeming lion-maned powerful face of Dorne appeared in the crosshairs as the Leader came out exactly on schedule (of course!) for his midnight breath of air.

The Lieutenant's life and career peaked in the two tiny movements of a finger slipping through the trigger guard and a thumb on the focus rotor. The image sharpened into pore-clear detail, and, as the thumb moved to the second rotor, zoomed to fill the frame with that detested about-to-laugh countenance, its muscular cheeks, the hint of crow's-feet around the wide-spaced brooding eyes. The joining of the crosshairs settled on the bridge of the Leader's nose, the finger tensed on the trigger, the image steadied—

And went out.

Went out, was blank, was gone.

There was a split-second then of endless time, a black universe composed entirely of total disbelief, and then he moved his eye back, which did nothing but emphasize the blackness with the dim presence of the arrow-slit. He slid his hand away from the trigger guard and up along the 'scope to the lens, to find what was obscuring it.

It was a hand. He had time enough to touch it and know it for what it was, when something blunt-pointed struck him on the side of the Adam's apple. He fell, the gun seemingly fastened into the darkness by darkness, staying suspended while he fell away from it, fighting for two impossibilities—breath, and silence. His knees struck the stone floor, and as he bowed his head over the agony in his throat, something struck him across the exposed nape, and he went down. Pain was a brief blaze of even darker darkness, which swallowed him up.

Time skipped a beat then. He was never to remember how he had been moved from a collapsed heap on the floor under the window to a sitting position against one of the side walls. Either it was still dark, or he was blind . . . no; it was just the dark, for he was aware of the dim arrow-slit. His eyes felt scalded. He had not cried for years, not since his father and two brothers had been taken by a patrol one night, never to be seen again; he had been only a toddler then. What touched him now was all the anguished grief and loss and frustrated anger he had denied himself during these careful years; he was, for the moment, denied anything else. The one thing he did not feel was shame, and that was supplied shockingly as soft cloth touched a cheekbone, one eye, the other, wiping away tears. No one should have known he had tears. He tried to raise two angry hands and could not; tingling agony in a spot just above each collarbone told him the nerves had been expertly pinched, and he knew from experience that his arms wouldn't belong to him for a while.

Something ringed his head, settled over his brow and eyes. He gasped. The light, as lights go, was not bright, but any light at all in this place was a dazzle. Understanding was a dazzle too—that these were blacklight goggles—a UV converter, and that with them and the invisible beam from the lamp between the lenses, he had been watched from the moment he entered the stone room in the battlement. He had been seen—photographed?—assembling the weapon and taking his aim. He had been, oh God, seen weeping, and his tears had been wiped away so that he could see through these goggles.

See what? A bright blur, a blink, a leather-backed escutcheon bearing the Leader's ubiquitous face, and on each side of it a letter, a scintillant S. Secret Service—Dorne's own legendary, mysterious secret service, above the law, outside the law; for even Dorne's law, made by Dorne, represented restrictions on Dorne, and Dorne was a man who would not be restricted.

He nodded, and the goggles were immediately snatched away. Three soft footfalls in the darkness, a breathless moment of waiting, listening, and then the heavy door was opened just far enough to build a black silhouette which slipped outside and closed the door again.

The Lieutenant gaped at where the swift vision had been, and tried not to think—thinking was too terrifying, thinking led to the certain knowledge that he was a dead man, and the even more destroying knowledge that he had been played with like a kitten and backhanded aside like an insect. So much for half a lifetime of care and passion. So instead of thinking he felt—felt the tingling above his collarbones descend to his biceps, forearms, hands, fingers, less an agony each second, until an effort of will was rewarded by a movement in his fingers. He got his hands up and shakily rubbed them together until they belonged to him again; then he pressed himself to his feet and followed the example which had just been set him; he went to the door and held his breath, listening. Nothing. He opened the door a very small crack, peered, slipped out, closed it. No one in sight. He turned to the right and began to walk.

If he had expected the battlement to be in a state of alert or alarm, he was disappointed. It came to him, as he passed a courier, who saluted, and then a noncom, that he had seen their faces at pretty much these places time and again before; that he had slipped back again into his accustomed slot in the intricate workings of the concentric guard. Since he had

come on watch tonight he had made his routine contact
points each a few seconds early, until he had accumulated a
shade under six minutes ahead of schedule. With these six
minutes and a weapon it had taken years to design and build,
he had meant to change the world. He now knew it had taken
no more than that to become useless and dead, leaving the
world, Dorne's world, unchanged and triumphant; for he was
right on his posted schedule. He could go straight to the
common room and turn over the watch to his relief, and
check out, and no one would know that life and all the
reasons for living had been drawn out of him, folded up, filed
away—in something less than six minutes.

In the familiar common room, full of familiar faces, he
checked across the columns of his report (one was headed
Unusual Occurrences, one *Unauthorized Personnel*; he lied
and wrote None, none, none all across the page; what could
they do to him now, for lying?) and could appreciate the
momentum of familiarity. You could be preoccupied, tired,
drunk and do familiar things right. You could be dead. He
knew he was watched, as he had been watched. He knew he
was more than helpless—he was futile. He turned over the
shift to Riggs, a career lieutenant with prominent front teeth
and a giggle, and went out into the floodlit night and checked
himself out through the familiar gate; and would this be the
last time? Perhaps, perhaps not—so much depended on how
amusing "they" found the game.

The familiar car was waiting, familiar Zein and Hallowell
and Iturbi were climbing in as he reached it, and as the car
slid silently along the dark streets, the talk was as usual.
Nobody noticed his silence; he was not a talkative man.
Iturbi was dropped off. More silent sliding and the new
familiarity of the Zein-Hallowell conversation; they always
talked about Iturbi. Then they were dropped off at the
Shrine of the Leader—they both lived near it, and the car slid
away northward on Dorne Boulevard, with the final familiarity of his silent occupancy of the wide rear seat, and the
familiar silent presence of the driver.

Northward on Dorne Boulevard?

"Hey!"

The car immediately slowed and drifted to a stop against the curb. Well, at last something was different to mark the day of his death. The driver had forgotten that he lived on the South Side. He peered. It was a woman. Well, most of them were. She half-turned toward him and said, "Come up front with me."

"I'll stay where I am," he snapped. "Turn this thing around and—" He stopped, thunderstruck, for with a single casual motion the driver hooked something out of her side pocket and tossed it back into his lap. It was the eyepiece of his telescope.

There was a moment of shattering silence—no repeat request or command, no display of weapons. She simply waited. The whole dialogue was there, back and forth, back and forth—argument, resistance, threat, fear. Then he did as he must—opened his door, got out, reentered beside her. The car started to move the instant the door clicked shut. He watched her face for a while by the wash and fade, the wash and fade of passing lights. Twenty-something, straight nose, good chin, large eyes—just another woman in uniform among the millions of the same. A thought occurred to him, a question. "Who jumped me in the battlement?"

"I did."

She drove with enormous competence and she seemed normally healthy, but she was not a large woman. Another few seconds of that silent dialogue: disbelief, could-it-be, who-else-then, *prove* it!—which she did in words: "You cried." Not what he wanted to hear, but proof enough.

She turned the car into a cross street and at last looked directly at him. "I don't blame you," she said. "I'd have done the same. I like you for it."

"Think of that," he said bitterly.

Ignoring this, she said, "You had no plans, had you, for afterward. After he was dead."

If she had asked him what his plans might have been, he

would have refused to answer. He might even have enjoyed dying for his refusal to answer. But this was a flat statement.

"Who needs plans? Dorne's a fool." The heretical words felt good after all these years of reverence. "Any man's a fool who builds his structure to a single kingpin. Snatch that out and the whole thing falls apart. It looks like strength but it isn't."

"And what did you think would happen when it fell apart?"

"I didn't care. Anything would be better than a controlled population living controlled lives. Something would come up out of the ruins—maybe not as neat, efficient, maybe not as comfortable. But it would be something alive and growing, not something perfect and—well, *stopped*."

She said, in a tone of perfect knowledge and certainty, "Dorne doesn't think he will live forever. He does think his system will. He's been ready for you for a long time."

"For me?"

"Or someone like you. Newton's first law operates everywhere, even in politics. 'Every action has an equal and opposite reaction.' If you create a society like this one, you create your revolutionaries right along with it. You know perfectly well there's an Underground."

"Don't try to tie me in with that pack of creeps!" he spat.

"Oh," she said, "I'm not. There are all kinds of revolutionaries, and the ones who make a lot of noise are the easiest to handle. They're noticeable—that's the thing. They can be found and picked off whenever the time is ripe. In addition, the people who follow them are usually misfits, and they don't stop being misfits just because they follow a new leader. They couldn't get along with the Establishment, and they can't get along with each other. Your 'kingpin' principle operates there, too. Eliminate the leader and you have only a mess to clean up, not a movement to put down."

"You have it all figured out," he said, his bitterness increasing.

She nodded serenely. He wanted to smash his fist into her

face—but not at seventy miles an hour on a winding road. Where was she taking him? The city was behind them now. She said, "There's another kind of revolutionary who's much more difficult to handle. He's the kind with a personal grudge, with the intelligence to plan his strike and the ability to carry it out. He has no partners or comrades; he can't be betrayed. The hardest thing of all to deal with is that he has a limited objective. He wants a single thing—let's say, to kill a man. He isn't building anything, he isn't saving the world, he doesn't even care if anyone ever finds out he's responsible. How can you guard against a revolutionary like that?"

"How did you?"

She smiled. "Just by knowing that he exists, that he's as inevitable as the man-the-barricades type of revolutionary hero. Once you know that, any Mark II or III computer can XT a portrait of him—who, why, how, when and where. All you have to do is sit and wait for him. He'll keep the appointment."

The wave of futility nearly drowned him. When it receded, he asked, "XT . . . that's—extrapolate."

"Right. That's what it's designed for—to predict. It takes all the known factors and casts probabilities, and compares all those and selects the most probable, and does it over again and selects the most certain of those, and so on. And we aren't using a II or III—ours is a VII. It talks to all the other computers. Lieutenant—it *knows*."

She pulled the car off the paved road and into a barely discernible dirt track through heavy forest. She stopped talking and concentrated on driving, tooling the car through unlikely gaps between trees and rock outcrops. It came at last to a cul-de-sac between a house-sized boulder and two giant Douglas firs. She braked to a halt. She made no move to open a door, and therefore neither did he. She must have touched a control somewhere because the ground on which the car stood began silently to rotate, as on a turntable. When the car was pointed between the tree trunks, the turntable stopped and she edged the car through. Looking back, the Lieutenant could see the turntable rotating back to its previous position.

"Come in." He looked at her, and then where she pointed. A hunter's shack on pilings, frame and tarpaper, built against a rock wall. He looked back at her. Starlight and a sliver of moon gave only a little light, but it was enough for him to see the confident way she moved as she came round the car and stood near him. She was taller than he had supposed, and she carried her hands a little away from her body, and her feet were placed so and just so. He realized there was no need to wonder if she had a weapon. Her hands were weapons—*she* was a weapon. And for all he knew she might have had a gun as well. He nodded and led the way to the shack. At her gesture he pushed the door open and went in. She followed. She closed the door and a light sprang out from her hand. He saw a bunk, an old stove, rubble on the floor, some firewood. She kicked at the firewood and the wall behind it rolled massively upward, revealing a corridor slanting downward into the hillside.

The Lieutenant paused right there and looked back past her at the flimsy barrier of the shack wall, and then at her. How he telegraphed what flicked through his mind, he did not know. Did he tense, narrow his eyes, flex his hands, set his feet? He almost moved, but she said quietly, "Don't."

And caught, he had to shake a rueful head and relax. He asked a straight question, gesturing at the corridor. "If I walk down there, will I ever come out alive?" And she gave him what sounded like a straight answer: "That is entirely up to you." She made an 'after you' gesture, and he sighed and went down the corridor; thinking several things on several levels: *That is one hell of a lot of woman,* and *What's she got that's so special?* because he had seen many a prettier girl, some who seemed more intelligent, a whole lot that were more fun. . . . And under it all, *They've caught me and I am going to die in this place.* She passed him after the turn at the bottom of the ramp, looking up into his face, and opened a door. They went in.

Torture chamber? Mad scientist's liar, with rock walls,

steaming retorts, and traveling arcs zit-zitting? Secret martial court, complete with granite-faced officers and an empty prisoner's dock waiting just for him? None of this . . . a homey living room. Carpet worn but not shabby, a little rip in a lampshade. Big sofa, two big chairs, three well-chosen small ones and a matching table, a large desk cater-cornered. Home, not office or shop. A cheerful little man in his fifties sprang up and came around the desk with his hand out. "Lieutenant! I've been looking forward to this."

He took the hand by sheer reflex, and the little man, talking warmly, made a tiller of it and steered him over to one of the big chairs. He had his choice of sitting in it or falling into it; he sat, dumbfounded. "Dr. McHenry . . . !" Had this been the moment for small witticism, he might have added ". . . I presume." He could presume; this was one of the world's most famous faces, along with—oh my Lord, she was here too, Rachel Heinz McHenry; the Sunday-supplement cliché for this couple was "Twenty-first Century Curie." She was a biochemist, if you like understatements, and her husband was the greatest living computer theorist, which means mathematics, logic, language, cybernetics, philosophy, electronics, and a number of sidelines. He never got the chance to get to his feet to shake Rachel McHenry's hand; she was there to give it to him before he could even try, and was begging him to accept coffee. He refused, not because he didn't want it but because it was a little like having the Pope scramble you some eggs. The whole thing was watched in (he thought) an amused fashion by the uniformed girl, who seemed quite at home here, though he found himself wishing she would take off the Dorne hat, with its shiny bill and the foreign-legion curtain around the back. The Dorne short-winged cape suited her; the hat did not.

Dr. McHenry went back to his desk chair and sat down. He opened the flat center drawer and took out a yellow sheet and laid it down and said, "I'm going to come straight to the point, Lieutenant. Tonight you tried to kill Leader Dorne. I'd like to know how long you planned this."

Suddenly the little dash of pleased surprise evaporated, and this was a grim business again. "You know already. I understand you have access to a Mark VII XT."

"He designed it," snapped the girl—perhaps a little defensively. Dr. McHenry held up pacifying hands to both of them. "Please," he said. "You're not being grilled, Lieutenant. Call it a rhetorical question. I was leading up to something else. You don't have to answer."

"In that case," said the Lieutenant, "I'll answer it. I think I began planning it the day my father and two brothers didn't come back after some soldiers dropped by one midnight. I was thirteen at the time; I'm twenty-seven now. There isn't anything I've done that wasn't part of it—getting into the Service, qualifying for the Concentric Guard—everything. I have never married. I never learned to dance. Tonight it all came to a peak and you took it away from me. Now you know what I am and what I've done and how I feel."

Dr. McHenry leaned back in his chair and delivered an unprofessorial "Wow." His wife—it was almost ludicrous—said with what sounded like genuine concern, "You're sure I can't get you something?" The girl looked very sober. Dr. McHenry slid the drawer open and took out another yellow sheet. He glanced at it and said, "How much do you know about Leader Dorne? I mean who his folks were, how he grew up, all the things that made him what he is?"

"I've read the school books. Who hasn't? Visions as a child, flabbergasting his teachers, arguing down the professors when he was twelve—all that. I never bothered much with it. All I cared about was him *now*—his habits, his routines, where I could get at him."

"Then let me tell you some things you may not know. Dorne was born a Jew. His parents weren't Jewish; they converted just before he was born. They were hardshell Fundamentalists who wanted to go all the way into the Old Testament because they found the new one not orthodox enough for them. When Dorne got old enough to think for himself he shucked all that and became a Christian. Somewhere in his teens he was a Buddhist for a while, but that didn't last; there's not much in real Buddhism for a man who wants personal power. After that he turned away from religion altogether and got involved with communism. Very involved. It didn't take him long to become part of the inner circle.

"That lasted for quite a few years, and then the currents began to flow in the other direction. Dorne joined the opposition, turned in a lot of his friends, and before long was masterminding the so-called Swing to the Right of the 1990's. It wasn't a big step to turn that into what we have today."

"And we'll have it forever, thanks to you and your Mark VII."

Again McHenry held up the pacifying hand. "It's very important—vital—for you to understand what we're trying to tell you. Just remember what I've said about the Leader. I want you to notice especially the timing of the changes he went through. At first it was a matter of weeks, then months, then years."

"And now," said the Lieutenant glumly, "there'll never be another. He's too old to change."

"Very good. *Very* good," said Dr. McHenry with surprising warmth. "The very point I wanted to get across. Now: Rachel."

She came closer and perched on the arm of one of the big chairs; she looked like a plump bird. He was marveling again at the very idea that this legendary figure should think of making coffee for him when she dropped her bomb: "Lieutenant, I've found out how to make a man immortal." She paused. "Truly. Barring accident, a man can live forever."

The Lieutenant closed his eyes carefully and opened them again to see again, really believe this plump friendly little lady who was saying things about DNA and RNA molecules. "Hard to do, mind you, but easy to understand. The pattern, the blueprint of the whole human being is in every single cell of his body. Now in a newborn baby, the patterns are sharp

206

and clear, but as we grow older the lines of the blueprint get blurred as the cells are replaced. It's just the same thing as making copies of a tape. You can get beautiful copies with good equipment, but no matter how good it is, when you have to make copies from copies, you lose a little each time. And that's all aging is.

"But if you have the original tape, and make each copy from that one, you can get a great number of almost perfect copies. Likewise if you have a tissue sample of a newborn baby, and keep it for, say, forty years, you can use it as a master to clean up the blurred lines in that same person's DNA molecules. It's done through the lymph system—flooding the tissues . . . oh, but never mind that, we don't have to get technical. Will you believe me if I say we can do it?"

"I'll believe you." He had to say it.

McHenry opened his drawer again and took out a yellow sheet. This was beginning to irritate the Lieutenant. Dr. McHenry beckoned the girl, who crossed to him, glanced at the paper, and then came to the Lieutenant. She sank to her knees before him, took both his hands, looked deep into his eyes. Holding him so—and her eyes seemed to be doing most of the holding—she pressed his hands down on the arms of his chair. There was a faint click and he looked down to find his wrists, his forearms and his thighs encircled by bands of silvery-gray mesh which flicked up and around and down into the chair again. "It's all right," the girl said before he could speak, could shout. "Try to relax, now." She stood up, moved away.

The Lieutenant gazed disgustedly down at his trapped limbs. "And now it begins, I suppose." He hoped his tone of disgust covered all of his terror.

"Nothing begins," said Dr. McHenry. "It's just time to tell you something, and we don't want you to get hurt." He looked at his wife, who said quietly, "We have a preserved sample of Leader Dorne's tissue, taken when he was only eight days old. We've been able to reconstitute the DNA from it, and prepare enough synthetic DNA to flood his whole

body. We are going to make him into a perfectly self-perpetu-
ating organism. We will make him immortal."

The Lieutenant yelled then, and leapt upward against the
straps. And again. And again. He began to shout something
with such force that the words could not be understood.
Saliva flew; he bit his tongue; blood flew. The women ran to
him, saying soothing nonsense words as to a hurt child,
wiping his wet and bloody mouth. Rachel McHenry bathed
his temples and eyelids with a tissue drenched in something
cool and medicinal. At last he was calm enough to be able to
use words, though he still shouted. "Don't you see what
you've done? You've killed us all, and all the people to come.
Oh, the armies and factories and farms will keep on going,
and all the people in them, but they'll be dead, all mankind
will be dead because it can't grow, it can't change! Why
didn't you leave me alone? Why didn't you let me kill him?"
He sobbed; then he shouted again: "What's in it for you?
Haven't you got enough medals and prizes already? What can
Dorne do for you?" After that he began to curse. They let
him. Dr. McHenry took another yellow sheet out of the
drawer. When he looked at it, he smiled. He handed it to
the girl, and the expressions which chased themselves over her
face were a sight to see—surprise, laughter, and then an
exquisite wave of pink. She returned to the chair and knelt
before the prisoner, waiting. When he began to run down, she
asked him gently, "Will you listen to me?" She had to repeat
it before he could hear her; he slumped back and glared at
her redly. She said patiently, "If I let you go, will you listen
to me?"

Still he stared, and she sighed and took from a pocket the
leather-mounted I.D. she had displayed in the stone room—
the profile of the Leader flanked by the two S's. "This isn't a
real one. We made it. Don't you see, we're not on Dorne's
side—*we're on yours.* You and I, all of us here—we want the
same thing; we want an end to what Dorne has built." She
threw the I.D. back over her shoulder, a used-up thing. He

followed it with his eyes, and then looked angrily at her again. "Why should I believe you?"

"Why did you believe I was in the SS? Just because I showed you that? What was I to do—explain all this to you, in the state you were in? Suppose I had—how far could I have gotten marching you out at gunpoint? They'd have caught us both, for sure. No, you had to leave by yourself, certain you were watched. The only thing that could make you do that was to believe the SS was on to you. Don't you see—I had to do it this way?" She was pleading with him, and while fury and amazement circled around his confused mind, she reached up and removed the Dorne hat, and did something with pins, clips . . . her hair cascaded down around her shoulders and back and breasts, such masses of red-gold hair as he had seldom seen, never touched—never in his stark, unswerving, purposeful life. "May I let you go now? Will you listen? Will you please listen?"

He nodded. Instantly she touched a control in the chair arm, and the restraints flickered out of sight. Rachel Mc-Henry said, "I could maybe make you that cup of coffee now?" and somehow they all laughed—not heartily, just a little, but it cleared the air.

McHenry came round his desk and crossed to the chair where the girl still knelt, like a nymph under a waterfall, a red-gold light-fall. He carried one of his yellow papers with him. He said, "Think, now—think hard. Remember what I told you about Dorne's patterns. He moved from religion to religion, then into politics, from one kind to another. He was looking for answers, he was looking for some law, some system that would be right for him, and finally, when he couldn't find one, he made one.

"But it is the pattern of that man to change. True, the changes came more and more slowly as he grew older, and true, too, that with a normal lifetime he would die before the next change could come. If he dies now, there will be no change. He has computers too, you know—and he has

programmed them. He will no longer be kingpin—his computer will run the whole structure, and *then* there will be death
for us all. Life itself is growth and change, and a society
which does not grow and change is dead, and all the people in
it, as you yourself said.

"Now we have given Dorne unlimited life, and because he is
what he is, he will change this thing. Ultimately he will
because he must—because he is Dorne and that is his pattern.
Also, he has more power to bring about the changes than
anyone else.

"All this will happen if he is immortal. He can't be
immortal as long as you are alive and free and determined to
kill him. Can you understand me?"

The Lieutenant looked from one to another of them, and
his eyes came to rest on the girl's hair. Rachel McHenry
murmured, "You have to find something else to live for."

The young man rose from his big chair and moved slowly
toward the girl. Almost like a sleepwalker he raised his hand
and gently touched her hair. The hand dropped away. He
shook himself, then said to Rachel, "Maybe I could. Maybe I
could, if. . . ."

No one finished the sentence for him, but the girl smiled.
The Lieutenant put his hands to his face for a moment, then
took them down, and now he could smile too, a little.
"You've batted me around like a ping-pong ball," he said a
little shakily. "I've never felt so helpless in all my life. You
people are out of my league."

"No we're not." Dr. McHenry smiled. "But our friend in
the corner is." He pointed at the battered desk—and why
should a Mark VII XT not look like a battered desk? "Don't
give us more credit than we deserve. Look at this."

Words were typed on the yellow sheet: *If killing Dorne is a
conviction, keep him. If an obsession—kill him.*

"Convictions yield to reason," McHenry said gently. "Ob-
sessions don't. It was a close thing."

The Lieutenant looked at that mass of red-gold and said,
"Not really." Nobody ever told him that the VII had

instructed her to take it down, that it had followed every word spoken in that room. Nobody ever told him, either, because it never occurred to him to ask, why a pair of Fundamentalist parents would preserve every scrap of flesh cut away from themselves or their child; such folk believe they will be reassembled on Judgment day, actually and literally.

So it was by this means that Mankind overpowered Death and conquered Time, and took the stars.

Suicide

Boyle . . . *jumped.* He did it. He really and truly did it. They say that when the end comes, no matter how swiftly, there's time enough for your whole life to pass before your eyes. That's not strictly true; it would take a real lifetime to do that, but there is time enough for a hell of a lot. However, Boyle discovered, as others had before him, that you get a lot of pictures, all out of order—yes, and sounds, too, voices speaking a word or two, laughing, a shout that reaches you at last from years away and means what the shouter meant instead of what you've always thought it meant. In such a moment everything makes sense. Some of the images and noises are apparently trivial: Aunt Edith saying "Please pass the salt" and how Hank always used to have one sock up and one down while they were little kids, and things like that.

Then there are the re-plays of things you know aren't trivial and never were, like the time you had to go to Scranton and Kay said suddenly "Don't go. Please don't go," and you knew damn well she was going to sleep with somebody that night and wanted you out of the way and yet she said that, and you—you went to Scranton anyway. And Kreiger saying, "Boyle, you know you'd be happier in some other line," which meant Out, never mind those years and all that sweat and loyalty and the pipedreams of the big desk with the opaline letters on a chock facing the door.

He jumped.

He jumped, and sure there was terror, there always is when you're falling, there often is when it's dark. And sure there was regret, and if-only-I-had-it-all-to-do-over-again. He had expected, and he got, a couple of brand new ideas to cure it all. Just walk up to him and say . . . just show her once and for all that he . . . take a loan on . . . a lot of stuff like that; and under and around it all, a deep glee: I made it. Boyle did not fail. *I said I would do it and I did.* That ought to prove something to the whole sonabitchin bunch of them.

That's about as far as he got before something in the dark took his foot and turned him. The wind was different as it whirled past his face and he found himself looking incredulously past his feet at the stars, with the great bulk of the cliff face blotting out a third of the sky. Then the lights (ten thousand lights in the valley below over his head, a million lights in the sky under his feet) were eclipsed by ten million more inside his head as he got a shower of cruel thumps and a hundred long numb scrapes that would be agony if he lived long enough for the shock to wear off, but he wouldn't.

And the lights went out.

"Don't go. Please don't go." The voice was soft and quite clear and close. He opened his eyes and could see the silhouette of her head as she bent close. He could even feel the stirring of the hairs over his temple stir to her breath. He blinked once and it wasn't her head or anyone's head, it was the bulk of the mountain against the sky. For a foolish flash he thought he might still be in midair, falling, but a single twitch of his cheek told him he was not. Falling through the unresisting air you do not feel pebbles and dirt ground into your flayed cheek. He shook his head to clear it and his whole body moved, slid. It was only a few inches, but it was enough to pack dirt and rubble into his collar and send a shocking stab of pain from somewhere low on his right leg right up through his body. Or maybe it was down. Up was still down for him. Cautiously he looked over his head and saw lights . . . stars? No, for they were in rows and patterns. They were the same as the lights on the valley floor. They were the lights of the valley floor.

He was lying on a spur of the mountain, on his back and head down, and the ground under him was tilted like a pitched roof. He looked quickly past his feet and there were the stars—and again he slid an inch or two. He suddenly and appallingly realized that if he twitched like that once or twice more, if he slid just far enough, fast enough so he did not stop, he was going to go right over that ragged edge down there.

Slowly and very carefully he studied out where his hands were. One was on the ground at his side, the other across his stomach. He raised this one and put it to the ground too. The left hand could find only loose pebbles and earth which slipped up (down) past him hopping and hissing when he moved his fingers, and bounded away into black space somewhere past his head. Not very far either. The right hand rested on what seemed like a more solid piece of rock. Carefully, not daring to turn his head to look, knowing it was too dark to see anyway, he explored it with his fingertips.

There was an edge there . . . more—it was a crack an inch wide. He could not discover how long it was nor how deep. He curled his fingers into it and it felt wonderful. He stopped moving for a time and indulged himself in the joy of feeling it. He had known this feeling once before when he had bought his first new car. *This is mine, this belongs to me.* He let his fingertips creep in and slide out again, very much the way he had let his proud hands stray over the new-smelling upholstery and dashboard. How wonderful to own a crack in a rock.

He tried to hook his heels into something and edge himself uphill a bit, but there was nothing but loose dirt and pebbles up there and an explosion of pain from his right leg. And his whole body told him it was about to slip again toward that edge, down (up) there past his head.

He got his right fingers as deep as they would go into the

crack, and stopped to think. The fear began then, and it wouldn't let him think. It rose and flooded over him and left him weak, with puddles of it here and there over his whole soul like tidal pools. He knew there would be other waves of it, too. Fear numbs your brain, fear can weaken, can paralyze your fingers, can draw them out of that precious crack in the rocks which is the only possession left to you in the head-down, lumpy, sliding universe.

He bit his teeth together until they hurt. It was a pain different from the other pains which vised and racked and skewered him, because it was a pain he did himself and could shut off himself. That may seem like a small thing, but it isn't. When a helpless man finds he can do anything—anything at all—he isn't helpless any more, even if the thing he does is useless. It was a strange thing he began to do. He began clenching and unclenching his jaw, and he found it was like a pump, emptying him of fear. He knew he could never get it all down to the last drop, but he didn't need that; he just wanted to get rid of enough of it so he could think again.

Slowly he brought his left hand across his body and as far as he could toward the right. The one hand found the other and the straining fingertips explored the ground next to it. The crack was full of dry dirt, and he dug clumsily to remove it. The effort increased the pressure of his whole body to slide, and the rock under his right hand began to press back. He realized suddenly that the right hand would tire, would simply wear out and quit, if that pressure grew much larger or lasted too long. He sank his left fingers in the crack as deep as they would go. He had to rotate his body slightly for this, and all his plans to move slowly and carefully evaporated in another great wash of terror as his body started to slide. He half sat up and whipped over to get his hands side by side into the crack. His body slid around the two hands as a pivot point and all around him, loose rocks moved in a small cascade, rustling and whispering and ending in a terrible silence just downslope from him as they leaped out into black space. When at last all movement ended he was lying belly-down, with both hands deep in the crack, and he couldn't see anything any more. But at least his head was upslope, and that seemed to do something for him.

He wheezed for breath and spit out dirt. He lay there panting until it hurt a little less to breathe, and he was immediately sorry for that, because the relative relaxation made him able to inventory other sensations. The one which rose over all others like a shout above a murmur was his right leg. He could feel nothing with it but a great constant blare of agony. Something very awful had happened to that leg.

His other one seemed all right. He shifted it a little. He could feel the knee grinding into the mountain, and the shin, but nothing below that. He waggled his foot. He felt nothing with it, and then realized with dreadful clarity that his two feet were projecting over the edge of the precipice.

The realization brought another great towering surf of fear. He used what he had learned about that: when terror comes you dig in and hold hard and let it roar past and slither back. Don't drown, don't let go. In a second or a minute or perhaps in an age or so, fear will subside. Even if it leaves pieces of itself through and through you, you will, sooner or later, get to where you can think again.

He resettled the grip of his two hands and pulled. His body slid painfully a fraction of an inch and he heard the beginnings of that whispering rustle as pebbles and dirt began to slide all around him. *Well slide if you want to,* he told them madly, *I'm not going to.* He went the other way—he went *up.* Not much, not quickly, and certainly, not easily.

When he drew his feet up over the edge, he was penalized bitterly—and richly rewarded. The pain in his right leg, when the foot touched the slope and turned, was far past anything he had ever known in all his life, and he cowered down under it and begged it not to make him faint and loosen his grip. But the left toe, seeking like some blind animal, found a little purchase and sent help like a regiment of cavalry in a cowboy-and-Indian picture *ta-taaa!* and helped his crackling fingers to move him uphill.

It was one of the most glorious moments he had ever known when he drew himself up so his lips were even with his hands. Driven by some impulse he could never have explained, he laughed a short hoarse laugh and put his tongue into the crack of the rocks between his hands. Then he lay there quietly, half-dozing, half-smiling, until it was time to move again.

Now the pulling was a pushing, as he pressed the crack down his body, past his chest, past his stomach. When his hands were fully extended downward he rested again, and then began to draw his left leg. He didn't dare raise himself to his knees yet, and had to bring the leg out and sidewise until his hip-joint all but whimpered for him to stop, but he would not.

Most grudgingly the left leg began to take the burden, and the more it straightened out the more able it became. He slid upward. He dared to reach forward and found a few shreds of grass—no help in themselves but their roots were a tight hummock. He felt it shift when he pulled, so he took it very easy. He got both hands on it and let his left foot say a heartfelt thank-you and good-bye to the crack in the rock, and drew it upward again.

The slope was a little less here and he found it possible to draw his knee straight upward instead of to the side as before—a luxury, an elegance, to be able to do that. His right leg was molten torture. He gritted his teeth against that; he said to himself, *now I've just got to switch that off.* You do not, of course, switch off the pain of a broken leg. You act as if you could, as if you had. Then somehow you can keep moving.

The slope now was still easier. He stopped to look up. This must have been about where he struck and slid after he jumped. He could not see very well—there was only starlight and the dimmest possible glow from the valley lights—but the cliff above him rose up impossibly sheer, and the nearby level spur on which he lay was not very wide—perhaps fifteen or twenty feet.

He crawled up to the base of the cliff and turned gingerly over, lifting his broken leg with both hands, and let himself down with his back to the rock.

He was so tired and so winded, and in such pain, that the distant lights blurred and whirled; and yet the simple act of sitting, of actually sitting down and leaning back against something, made him feel favored to the point of luxuriousness.

Then it all disappeared into a black and comfortable slumber before he could get it sorted out in his mind.

When he awoke it was in the gray suggestions of false dawn and fevered dream. For a moment he clutched the earth to right and left, and looked across the valley with vertigo—so far away, those lights, so far down. Then the memory flooded back of those minutes—hours, was it?—when he lay on his back with his head downhill and one hand in a crack in the rock, and he looked around him as he sat with his back against the cliff, and almost smiled.

He rocked back and forth to get the blood circulating in his buttocks and legs, and then pressed and clawed himself upright, grunting against the stabs of pain. He rested a moment, standing, then fumbled his fly open and urinated. He didn't push, he just let it happen. There was something very wonderful about the sound of it and the faint, warm, familiar acrid smell. It wasn't that anything was running out of him; it was more that something alive was happening here, and it was important just because of that.

When he was finished he zipped up and looked to right and left. Tumbling rainwater had carved an angled gully down to the shelf on which he stood. It wasn't smooth nor wide nor especially safe—some of it looked like loose and crumbling earth rather than rock—and it was steep.

He began to climb it.

He climbed for nearly five hours. It was only about sixty

feet. Once he had to stop to build a road—a road of pebbles and root-ends and a rock or two, anything he could reach and pack in, a road all of four feet long. Once he slept for a time, twice he fainted when earth fell away from under him and he had to leap to save himself, twisting his injured leg.

And in the fourth and fifth hours something strange happened to Boyle. He began to hurry.

It was the hurry that caused the second of these faints, and when he recovered he had to crouch there for a time and think it out, and wonder why he had hurried, because if there was no reason, then it wasn't smart to go on hurrying, right?

All he could think of was that he wanted to make the top before anyone could come to help him. He didn't understand that at all, so he put it out of his mind, but he stopped pushing quite so hard.

But when he reached the top, he couldn't make it. There was no way to make it. The little crooked sometimes-there, sometimes-not, sometimes-rock, sometimes-earth gully ended in a narrow crack in an overhang.

Boyle sat down under the overhang and looked out over the valley. It was daylight now and all but a few of the lights were gone. The sun wasn't up yet but the distant skyline was black and sharp, and the sky above it had turned from gray to pearl and was beginning to show a cast of pink. He looked up at the underside of that overhang and he suddenly began to get mad.

Among the rubble lying around was a narrow pointed flat stone about eighteen inches long. He picked it up and hefted it, and then began to dig at the overhang. He dug in and up, and earth fell away and went hissing down, and he dug some more. He got expert very quickly on how much he could dig before lumps and clumps of it would fall away. He uncovered some roots and dug around them until, farther in, they weren't threads and strings, but rods and bleached boughs— something to hold to while he reached further, dug deeper.

His arms and his back and the left leg which was bearing all his weight began to ache, and then it was more than an ache, it was something that strove to match the torture of his broken right leg. He seemed to be operating some weird sort of contest to see if he could make the rest of his body hurt as much as that leg. He delved inward making a sort of cave into the cliffside, knowing perfectly well that if he undercut enough he had more than an even chance of bringing the whole thing down on himself and going with it into the valley; but the odds suited him and he wouldn't quit.

For the hundredth time he looked up to gauge the soft material over his head, and when it happened he almost didn't see it—didn't see that the ceiling above him was abruptly lower. It was actually moving when he dropped his stone tool and grasped roots with both hands, twisting them around his wrists and hanging on with all his might.

Almost silently the overhang collapsed, and for a black choking moment he was totally certain he had buried himself. Then the crushing weight slid off his back and he heard the rumble of earth and rocks receding downhill, and shook his head free, and opened his eyes.

There was no more overhang. Where the rain-gully had begun in a narrow slit, there was a wide V, slanting down from the top in a natural 2 to 1 slope, and full of roots. He bellied into it and clawed his way to the top and (with a kind of joy) thirty level feet further before he collapsed.

He lay there for a long time without even trying to think. Then at last he rolled over, handling his hurt leg as if it was a fragile possession of someone else's, and sat up to look across the valley at the tip of the sun as it pressed up out of its slot behind the hills. All it said to him was that this was a new day, and he didn't have to think about that a lot.

What he did think of, as he sat there in his new day waiting for someone to come along, was the two questions he *hadn't* asked himself, not for a second, during all those terrible hours:

Why had he jumped?

Why had he climbed?

Just sitting here, watching the sun come up—that was all the answer he needed for the second one.

And the first one just didn't matter any more. *Right?* he asked himself. "Right," he said.